I Used
to Believe
I Had Forever
Now I'm Not
So Sure

I Used
to Believe
I Had Forever
Now I'm Not
So Sure

by William Saroyan

COWLES

To the guard at the ruins of the
Monastery of the Roses, near Erivan—
old, indestructible, nameless, and the nation.

Note

This is a book of 52 short pieces, written over a period of 34 years by the same man, now approaching the end of his 60th year. Among the pieces there are short stories, short plays, essays, and poems. 60th year? Impossible. There must be some mistake. It must have been somebody else. I was always young. (Or was I always 60?) Anyhow, the pieces can be read in consecutive order, or at random. Most have appeared in print somewhere or other, but many haven't. All have been revised to suit the purposes of a book, and many have been given new titles.

William Saroyan July 14 1968 Fresno, California

Contents

I Used
to Believe
I Had Forever
Now I'm Not
So Sure

The Saroyan Prizes, 1908–1940

This "poem" appeared in *The New Yorker* magazine dated August 31, 1940. On that day I had lived 32 full years, right down to the last minute. The years had been wonderful, all things considered, so that at 32 I was not disenchanted with either the human race or the world. I loved them both. (So what about now? Well, I still love them both, more deeply than ever, but perhaps not quite so helplessly, rather more deliberately.)

I began to send stuff to magazines soon after I paid $13 for an Underwood typewriter in Fresno in 1921 when I was just thirteen, almost fifty years ago, but I don't believe I have offered stuff to *The New Yorker* magazine more than a dozen times. Three times the magazine has taken what I have offered: two short stories, and this poem.

I have always enjoyed seeing a new issue of *The New Yorker*, both for the funny pictures and for the writing. It is surely the most interesting general weekly in the world, perhaps of all time. It gets fat in the autumn and skinny after the new year. It runs a lot of interesting ads, which I enjoy as one enjoys poetry, fiction, history, drama, and critical writing.

I never became a *New Yorker* writer. There was always good money in it, and I always liked the idea of earning good money at work I wanted to do anyway, but I never believed I belonged in that group, or neighborhood, or club, or whatever you might care to call it.

Another group that had no appeal for me was the one that frequently gathered for lunch at the Algonquin Hotel. The last survivors of this group still believe that the things they said fifty years ago are witty. They're dreaming. The stuff was *always* dull.

1

Having been awarded prizes,
Ribbons, money, honors, invitations,
And other things,
I, William Saroyan,
Born August 31, 1908,
In Fresno, California;
Student at Emerson Public School
On L Street, between San Benito and Santa Clara;
Holder of the First Prize for Street Sales,
The Fresno Evening Herald, 1917;
Twice Winner of the Around-the-Block Race, 1918;
Founder, Manager, and Boss of Henry-and-
Willie's Empty Lot for Sons of Armenians,
Assyrians, and Other Immigrants;
Winner of Highest Third-Grade Binet-Simon Intelligence
        Rating,
"Far Above Average, Although Poor at Arithmetic;"
Official Letter-Writer to Mayor Toomey
For the Fifth Grade;
Speaker at the First Meeting
Of the Parent-Teachers' Association;
Singer of "The River Shannon;"
Author of "How I Earned My First Dollar;"
First to Dive from the Oak Tree
Into Thompson Ditch at Malaga;
First to Climb Guggenheim's Water Tank
And Drop a Cat;
Most Frequent Visitor to the Public Library;
Borrower of the Most and Best Books;
First Reader of the Autobiography of Benjamin Franklin;
First to Subscribe to Lionel Strongfort's
Body-Building Course;
Holder of the Certificate for Freehand Penmanship;
Fastest Postal Telegraph Messenger
In the San Joaquin Valley, 1921,
And Other Things Too Recent,
Or Too Numerous to Mention,
Award:
To the leaders of the English, French,
German, Italian, Spanish, Russian,
Jewish, Japanese, Chinese, Balinese,
Arab, Afghan, African, American,
And all other peoples,

For their superhuman acceptance
And extension of stupidity,
Lying, and conniving
As a basis for correct human behavior—

11¢

To all soldiers, excepting professionals,

For their skill at marching,
And for their pathetic faith
In killing and dying for nonsense,
Or at least for nothing they can understand—

One cancelled air-mail stamp.

To all intellectuals,

For the effectiveness with which
They have introduced the truths and beauties
Of art into life
And saved the living from disgrace—

One plugged nickel.

To the Church, in all its variations,

For its noble influence everywhere—

One oyster-shell button.

To you, for being fond of me—

Any prize you like,
Any colored ribbon,
Any amount of money,
Whatever honor you please,
An open invitation,
My typewriter, my cornet, my bicycle,
All my letters from important people,
All my prizes, ribbons, medals, honors, awards,
As well as the things you care about.

A Seaside Friendship

A Seaside Friendship was written for a small newspaper syndicate named Spadea in 1956 for $100 cash on the barrel-head, as the saying is. It appeared in perhaps as many as three dozen newspapers throughout the country, one or two big, as in Boston and Chicago, but most of them little, often weekly, and very local. Being about a dog, a lot of readers wrote to me in care of the various newspapers, to tell me about *their* dogs. In those days I had a lot of divorced-wife support to pay every month, I owed a lot of back taxes, and money for myself was always in short supply. Whenever money was all gone, I wrote a piece and sent it to the small newspaper syndicate, and a few days later received a check for $100. The piece was worth more, but I needed a few bucks quickly, so I let it go. I did a lot of walking on the beach at Malibu, talking to myself, to the sea, the sky, the great rocks, the pebbles, the sea gulls, the live seals, the dead sharks, and the dogs that came up to tag along. This was one of six or seven such dogs, but I still remember her with a particularity that is understandable, for she was quite simply a very real personality.

One of my best friends on the beach at Malibu is a dog I call Laughing Girl, although her name is Cinderella. The name is stamped in metal on her dog-tag or license. She is a three-year-old German Shepherd and we have been friends ever since she was brought to the beach two years ago. She lives with a family a mile up the beach from my house, and although I've never met the family I've seen the two little girls and the young mother and the young father. They're very nice people, and they have a very nice dog.

Two years ago I was on the beach picking up pebbles when Laughing Girl came up to see what I was doing. Well, I was picking up pebbles and putting them in my pocket. The tide of the Pacific at Malibu was coming and going, the way it always does, and I was out there getting a little air and exercise. Laughing Girl watched for ten minutes, and then she picked up a rock about twice the size of a hen's egg. She had no pocket, and for a moment she didn't know where to put the rock.

I said, "I'll be glad to take the rock." Laughing Girl thought about this a moment, and then she put her nose into my hand but didn't drop the rock.

"Dogs don't collect rocks," I said. "Let me have it."

She looked up and with her eyes said, as if she spoke flawless English, "My rock."

"O.K.," I said. "But what are you going to do with it?"

Laughing Girl replied instantly. Holding her head high she walked out into the tide, turned around to make sure that I was watching, and then with considerable ceremony and earnestness she dropped the rock into the sea.

She then came romping out of the water, took hold of my arm with her teeth, then my ankle, and then she challenged me to race her up the beach. Well, I was forty-five then and no match for a dog, but I gave it a go, and Laughing Girl won going away. She came back, though, and suggested we chase sea gulls. We did that for a while, but I wasn't really much good at it. And of course half the fun is barking, and I'm not much good at that, either. All the same, I had a nice time.

A few days later I decided to take a long walk, and Laughing Girl decided to go along. She was all dignity that day, walking beside me slowly. When I stopped to look far out at the sea, Laughing Girl stopped to look, too.

"Water," she said.

And when I stopped to study a glassy blob of life that had been washed up onto the beach Laughing Girl studied it, too, and then she said, "What is it?"

"That's one of the many rudimentary forms of life in the sea," I said. "You may notice at the center of it the makings of a rather simple but nevertheless miraculous piece of digestive machinery."

Laughing Girl pressed her nose upon the glassy blob, and then drew it away quickly.

"Gooey," she said.

5

About half a mile up the beach she stopped to study something else. When I reached her she looked up and said, "Fish."

"Yes," I said. "That's a baby shark. The surf fishers don't care for them. They just throw 'em up on the beach."

We had a lot of walks and talks, and then I went to New York on business. I was gone two months. When I got back I went for a walk and far up the beach I saw Laughing Girl standing and looking out at the sea, as I had done so many times. I was fifty yards away when she turned and noticed me. She went into a panther crouch, and as I drew nearer she began to move toward me, every muscle in her handsome body tight and alive. For ten or twenty yards she moved cautiously, her body low, and then suddenly she turned herself loose and was on me in a leap. She took my arm in her teeth, and then my ankle, and then she searched around until she found a rock about twice the size of an egg. She picked it up, looked at me, walked out into the tide, dropped it, came back, and said, "Remember?"

"Of course I remember," I said.

We walked along, and it was great.

Emerson has a rather wonderful essay on friendship. It's certainly one of the nicest things.

Pebbles on the Beach

Pebbles on the Beach tells something more about my life on the beach at Malibu. I was unavoidably in the general vicinity of Hollywood, with its preposterous people and values, and I had to see about not letting it bother me too much. Being on the beach helped. The piece was written in 1952, and under another title came out in *Art News*. The thing about the piece is that it keeps some of the truth I knew at that time on record. I have always felt that something of that sort is desirable, and as soon as I took to writing I began to write about where I was at the time and what I was doing. In one degree or another all of my writing marks passing time. Pebbles on the beach are marks of time. Each of them is also a thing of beauty and meaning for whoever happens to be there to notice. Frequently I came upon a patch of pebbles that made me feel I was in the presence of a congregation of people. A pebble is not unlike a face, and a crowd of people seems to be a sea of faces, as the saying is. I loved the pebbles. I loved getting out to them every day. But most of all I loved the sea.

I live in a small house on the beach at Malibu, quite close to the water, if not in fact upon it: high tide certainly brings the sea under the house. It also brings miscellaneous objects.

Some of the objects are man-made and may be dismissed: bottles of various kinds, light bulbs, old shoes, brushes, brooms, parts of furniture, and so on. There is form in many of the man-made things, and frequently it is good form.

The other objects are not man-made. They are sea-made, water-made, tide-made, time-made, sun-made, wind-made: pebbles and rocks, sea-trees and plants, shells, driftwood. These objects are made accidentally, inevitably, haphazardly, without plan, without beginning or end, without intention. Nature does not strain after art. It *is* art. Everything it does, or everything that is done to it, whichever happens to be true or truest, *is* art.

I collect the objects rolled up onto the beach by the sea.

I look at them, study them, have them around, turn them over to friends, lose them, or throw them back into the sea. I do this because it is satisfying, and because it is the means by which I get the small amount of exercise I need.

Mainly, I collect pebbles, but only because there are always more of them than there are of anything else. I think it is the simultaneous general sameness and infinite variety of rocks that appeal to me. Solely in the realm of size and shape rocks are very exciting. Add to this the matter out of which a rock is made, the probable manner of its making, the weight, color, and texture of it, and a student has a very great deal to notice.

My collecting has never been systematic, but it has acquired a free and easy method based on simple principles.

Three months after I moved into this house the front porch was loaded with pebbles of all kinds. A number of people said, "What are the rocks for?"

Each person was given an answer appropriate to his character.

"They are to remind me that art should be simple."

"They give me ideas for characters and stories."

"I like them."

"They are for throwing at people who ask what they are for."

A thing that is in space, as a rock is, is sculpture, or, if you prefer, *raw* sculpture. Now, imagine the enormous variety of sculpture to examine at one's leisure or whenever it is convenient, after only half an hour on the beach.

Let us say that out of the hundreds of thousands of pebbles on the beach the thoughtful collector has brought home only three or four dozens of them. He has run water over them and placed them according to size on the counter between the kitchen and the parlor—a counter that is a daily art gallery.

Now, he noticed each rock, each work of sculpture, when he picked it up. He noticed it again when he ran water over it. Again when he set it down on the counter. And he notices all of them together from time to time, whenever his glance happens to fall on them.

This nearness of these individual works of sculpture, and the gallery-group of them, is a source of great delight.

A natural thing has a soul, a personality, a reality, whichever you prefer. Certain rocks have souls more moving to the beholder than a good deal of man-made sculpture. Rocks do not even accidentally resemble other things. They resemble nothing. They are rocks. That is a very delightful thing. But of course there is always somebody who will pick up a rock and remark how like a fish or a seal it is. It would be a lot more nearly accurate to say of a rock that it is simultaneously preposterously simple and profoundly mysterious.

If it is possible for a rock to be a work of sculpture, an object of art, then what is an object of art? An object of art may be anything noticed in its entirety. Now, it happens that I am nearsighted. I see near things with great clarity. I must put on glasses to see far things clearly. Thus, it is quite natural for me to notice a rock clearly and in its entirety. It is this noticing of the rock that makes the rock an object of art. And the purpose of art may be said to be to impel careful and creative looking—at a given object, at anything, at everything.

Is there such a thing as creative looking?

Yes.

What constitutes such looking?

Clarity, intelligence, imagination, admiration, and love.

You make a point of looking at the object, you look steadily and clearly, you see the object, you see it again, you see it again, you notice the true nature of it in its entirety and in its parts, you relate its reality to all reality, to all time and space and action, you admire its survival, and you love its commonness and its individuality.

But the gifts of the sea are not rocks and pebbles alone. Its shells, whole or broken, are rich and rewarding. I am not thinking of the shell as the literal instructor it is to the sculptor. I am thinking of it as an object of art to observe for its own small sake. Again, the same order of shell may be collected by the dozens, and not two will be alike. This is always a delight to notice.

The fibrous trees of the sea are good to behold because by the time they are washed up onto the beach they have taken a beating from the sea, but are still beautiful. Their thick and knobby bases, which had seized upon rocks and fastened there, have been very slowly, very gradually, drawn away from the rocks by time and the gentle or violent play of water about them, and then they have been shoved and rolled around and about, perhaps for years, dislocated, dying, or dead, and then they have been rolled out of the sea.

Now, there are things from the land that are washed down hillsides in heavy rains, or in rivers, into the sea, and sooner or later some of these things find their way back to the land—driftwood, in particular. Roots of all kinds, washed and rubbed clean to the heart of their reality. Plain sticks, designed by erosion and washing. Branches, knobs, stumps. One of the best stumps I ever found must have weighed sixty pounds, and had fallen into a design which I did not expect to know fully in anything under three or four years, but somebody who came to my house when I wasn't home went off with it. There is no more unfair thief than the driftwood thief.

What about the man who doesn't live near the sea? Where is he to find nature's objects of art? Well, they are everywhere. Leaves, for instance. Leaves and twigs are not junk—they are objects of art.

Well, then is junk junk? Is man-made stuff junk? Not necessarily. Anything—anything at all—noticed particularly is not useless, it is useful. And an object of art is profoundly useful.

It reminds you that you are alive.

High Tide and Low Tide

High Tide and Low Tide was written on Monday February 11, 1957, or at any rate it was on that day that I ran through some of the notes I had made and typed them out. Some of the notes were old, some recent, but none had been used in a new work, and it seemed to me that I ought at least to have a record of them, to remember the ideas that had seemed interesting enough to be jotted down on the backs of envelopes. I have always found the notes of writers interesting. No other order of human activity seems to impel such a variety of ideas, although anybody's notes or reminders are interesting. A writer just naturally tends to be more interested in everything than anybody else. That's the business he's in. These notes did not appear in print, although in my third book, called *Three Times Three*, 1936, there is a long piece entitled Quarter, Half, Three-Quarter and Whole Notes. *The Yale Review* ran another assortment in 1938, and several small magazines have also published similar assortments. I jot things down all the time. So far I haven't knowingly taken something jotted down and put it into a new work. But it may very well be that unknowingly I have done so all the time, that every new work is rooted in an idea jotted down long ago, and apparently forgotten, but actually not. And many ideas that I have felt I could never possibly forget, and therefore did not jot down, I *have* forgotten. My father used to wake up in the middle of the night, I was told, to jot something down for a new poem, or his next sermon. Such things run in a family.

My Holiday at Paradise Cove, an earnest, laughing play.

America Lost: how a man loses piece by piece his country.

The Word: a book about what writers meant to me at the time.

The Lone Man's Visitors: Blake, Dostoevski, Mark Twain, Pancho Villa.

The Little Singer: the little bird on the backporch.

I'll Keep My Friends Only as Long as They're Willing to Remain Acquaintances, a story.

Let's Make a Play, a television program.

A Man Sensitive to Human Suffering.

World Without Beginning. (Never mind without end.)

The Country's Cut-ups.

World Conscience.

Names Are History. Greek: anama. Armenian: ahnoon.

What Do You Care?

In Kindergarten.

Letter to a New York Gossip.

The Sea and the Rocks.

Telephone Tricks: the clever calls of the famous movie actor, who pretends to be the police, a giveaway television program, an old friend, and so on: he calls pretty girls and keeps them on the line for hours.

How I Got Rid of My Time-Taking Friends.

What Did Corey Say?

The Frightening Past.

Here's the Answer.

The Lady Is a Pig.

The Rattlesnake Across the Road.

Blood Money.

The King of the Medicine Men.

Fifty-Fifty, a television program: for 50-year-olds only.

Let's Make Something. People send in "things" they have made, or descriptions of things needed.

Fox. The story of a movie theatre in a poor neighborhood of a big city, 1935–1955.

Genius Man.

Affection For a Failure: how the fire is taken out of a young spirit.

Cats and Dogs. (And the Dog that wanted to be Turned into a Cat.)

An Old Fool Like Me.

The 101st Day of the Year.

The Funny Man.

The Demand For Sympathy. (It is necessary to find no kind of human personality contemptible.)

The Little Red Heads. (The birds around the house.)

Old Clothes.

A Pipe-Smoking Slob.

How We Missed the Jitney Bus.

The Sea Gull on the Roof.

How Old Are You Today, Boy?

Ah, the Luxury of Time.

Whispered Song: I tremble when I see you smile,
　　　　　　　Tremble when I hear you speak,
　　　　　　　Tremble, tremble, love, when you sigh.

What Did You Dream in the Afternoon Sleep?

There Is Always Something the Matter.

The Big Men (a joke about the pretenders).

Make a Guess, a television program.

You Be the Judge, another.

The Clamor for Acclaim: the publicity racket.

Anxiety About Children, a play.

The End. (He says, "I don't know what happened. I was always so busy with something or other I didn't notice anything else.")

Now, In the Bars They are Drinking: all saloons, bars, taverns, cocktail lounges, city, town, village, highway, country: and the talk.

A Strong Will and a Weak Mind.

The Corner Where You Are, a play.

Journey: from entrance to exit, birth to death, plan to achievement.

A man says to his wife (of a great opera singer): "He's really in there trying, isn't he, honey?" Of pumpernickel: "This chocolate cake of yours is very nice." Old Unconscious.

The Lonely Lights (from trains).

Golden Days.

I never belonged to any group.

What I Missed.

A Merry Go.

Now, the way to take it is slow and easy
The way to take it is slow and easy
The only way is slow and easy
If you want to live right. (have fun)

The wife says, "Did you miss me?" The Husband says, "Yes, but it was a pleasure."

The Southern Charm Boy: he speaks with that odd and annoying inflexion that leaves every inane remark dangling in the air, demanding but never getting astonished attention.

The Man Who Wanted to be Hated. (He pretended to belong to any group that was being hated.)

Mercy and No Mercy.

An Unsavory Character.

For the Fun of It.

A Clever Son of a Bitch.

A New York newspaperman says, "I'm cracking with the boys, but I'm saying the wrong things all the time."

The Wind-Swept Sand of the Sea.

How to Live a Year at a Time: a book: 365 days, 52 weeks, 12 months. (How to divide a year for effective living.)

I may be a mess, but I'd rather be me than you, a song.

The Parade on the Beach.

How to do Nothing.

A New Night. (The Day has been pretty well taken care of: what man needs is new sleep, new dreams, new restoration.)

Nothing Man Nothing.

The Wheels of Memory

The Wheels of Memory was intended to be a kind of poem about man's restlessness, his migrations, his goings and comings. It was written in January of 1953, sent to a magazine, turned down, filed, and forgotten. An editor had invited me to send something to his magazine in connection with a general feature, along the lines of early travel. I very much wanted to oblige him, not only because I needed the money, but also because I believed I might just write something good, but the editor didn't want it. The going of this wagon is, in fact, my earliest memory, which I have always wanted to understand fully, so that I have tried to write it six or seven times during the past forty years, because the arrival of memory in a man is his real beginning, his real birth, and such a time must have continuous importance to him until the very time when he must hand memory back.

They go, with a ho for heaven, this place is ours no more, goodbye and don't forget.

The horse must have given them the idea for the wagon. Instead of a leg, a wheel here, another here, a third here, and the fourth here. And instead of the barrel-body a level floor—house, home and hearth on wheels, slow, but swifter than centuries and staying.

They *had* stayed, and then they'd said it's go or die, we've been here long enough, get your hat, Pa. We've tried, and half the time we've done all right, but this ain't it, Ma, there's something more, pick up your junk and shut the door, it's time to go. Where, though? Where is it different, and *how* is it different? We'll see, Pa. We'll see, Ma.

They go, and each of us goes with them, each of us remembers having gone, and some of the wheels and wagons.

The first wagon was in 1910, more for hauling than for people, but also for people, two on the seat, four in the back on the mattress, among the chairs, boxes, books, pots and pans. The Old Boy, less than a year from The End, speaking softly to the horse, old, lumpy, tired, and never much: "Giddap, Beauty. Go, now."

He was a kid then, thirty-six, but to the New Boy, only two years after The Beginning, he was old, and his father.

Beauty went, slowly at first, the wagon heavy, the wheels stiff from standing, and then little by little faster and faster, but never so fast a boy couldn't have beat her to town by a mile. She even stopped to nibble grass and stand and stare at a house, as if it were a place she knew and might like to go back to.

"All right now, Beauty, time to go."

Again she picked up her feet and went.

The New Boy watched and listened and thought as many things without words as may be found in books, and then he let the summer take him to sleep.

When he awoke it was another time, another place, the Old Boy was gone, but the New Boy, himself, was right there, and apparently he was there to stay.

Sunday Is a Hell of a Day

Sunday is a Hell of a Day appeared in *The American Mercury* in August 1957, but by that time *The American Mercury* had long since ceased to be the magazine founded in the early 1920s by H. L. Mencken and George Jean Nathan. The fact is that one of the first magazines I sent my writing to, from the front bedroom-study in the recently bought house at 3204 El Monte Way in Fresno, was *The American Mercury*. Others were *The Bookman, The North American Review, The Century,* and *Scribner's*. They have all long since disappeared, and so have a good many others. Mr. H. L. Mencken himself probably never read any of the essays or stories I sent him during the early years of *The American Mercury*, for if he had I am sure that when we met at lunch at his home on Hollis Street in Baltimore in 1941 he would have mentioned having seen my name on a piece of writing that he had found unpublishable. Whoever *had* checked my manuscripts had not seen fit to drop me a line about my writing, but had only attached a printed rejection slip to the manuscript, slipped it into the addressed and stamped envelope, and sent it back. It wasn't until I was 20 years old that any editor returned a manuscript with a letter. His name was in three parts, and I used to be able to remember it, but now I can't, although I believe the third part of it was Purdy. I had sent *The Bookman* from 2378 Sutter Street in San Francisco in 1929 the first chapter of a novel-in-progress called The Cat's Getting Fatter, and this very kind editor had dropped everything to sit down and type a very full and friendly reply. I kept looking for his name to appear on items in magazines, in anthologies, or on his own books, but I never found it. I saw it only once, at the bottom of his letter. I'm not sure I even wrote to thank him, but his letter had profound

17

significance in my life, and I continue to be grateful to him, whoever he was.

In 1935 when I visited Soviet Armenia (getting as near to Bitlis, the home of the Saroyans, as I could get without a Turkish visa, aged 26, and only 200 miles from the great fortress city in the mountains) I seldom knew what day of the week it was, because days, as days, were out of style there.

"Is this Saturday or Sunday?" I remember asking miscellaneous people.

They didn't know. They said, "Well, it's my fifth work-day." Or third, or fourth. Somebody said, "Tomorrow is my holiday." And so on.

I wondered if the numbering rather than the naming of the days was a good idea. Perhaps it was, or was meant to be. For instance, in Vienna, or perhaps Budapest, on Sunday afternoons a great many more people than on Tuesday or Wednesdays, for instance, committed suicide. There was no doubt in their minds, most likely, what day it was. It was Sunday, and Sunday means something to everybody. To many it means too much.

The day of rest, the day of the church, the day of no work is a wonderful day for many, and for others the toughest of all. It's the day of the sun, the day to get out into the light—to go for a drive, or for a walk. It's the day the kids go to Sunday School (if they go), and parents to church (if they do): but if they don't there's church stuff on the radio from very early in the morning straight through to midnight. And so it is with television, too. There is a quietude to the day that can be very attractive, but also very boring.

Sundays in Fresno were both pleasant and boring for me. Most of the time I hated going to The First Armenian Presbyterian Sunday School, but I went just the same, because it was the rule of the family. I didn't mind too much, because it was possible to have fun there, too. Everything was in English of course, except the major part of Reverend Knadjian's sermon, but we didn't stay for that very often. If we did we sat up in the gallery and counted bald heads and millionaires. There were around thirty bald heads to one millionaire. There were three millionaires, but they weren't halfers, they were full millionaires. How or why they'd become Presbyterians, I don't know. Things like that happen in a mysterious manner. The three millionaires of The First Armenian Presbyterian Church had good heads of hair. There was no connection, though, because so did ten times as many poor men. As for the women, they all had long hair.

At Sunday School one of us invariably requested Song Number 247, so we could sing, "At the bar, at the bar, where I smoked my last cigar, and the nickels and the dimes rolled away," instead of the proper words, which we didn't care for. The proper words of some of the songs we *did* care for, though, especially, "Leaning, leaning, leaning on the everlasting arms." We didn't understand the meaning of the words too well, but then we really didn't need to, and as we sang we took to leaning on arms that *weren't* everlasting. It was a good song, and still is. I put it into *The Human Comedy,* and I sing it two or three times a year, at least.

Sunday lunch after church—we never called it dinner—was always big and varied, with all kinds of stuff on the table: vegetables of all kinds stuffed with ground lamb and rice and herbs: matzoon, which became fashionable as yogurt: pilaf, which also became fashionable: meatballs stuffed with chopped onions, parsley, and pomegranate seeds: grape leaves wrapped around meat and rice again, baked in olive oil: white cheese, black olives, grapes, casabas, watermelons. And then small cups of pulverized coffee and rolled cigarettes in the parlor for grown-ups—uncles and aunts in town from their vineyards and orchards: not a millionaire in the lot, and one or two of the men bald, serene, and thoughtful, especially at the ritual of sipping the hot thick coffee and the rolling of the cigarettes. Memories of Bitlis would come forward in the Sunday talk, and somebody would remember the heroic work of the great Najari Levon who as a young man of seventeen was asked to run seventeen miles with an important message for an Armenian revolutionist who was hiding out in a nearby village. The message was written on a piece of cigarette paper. Najari Levon made excellent time, but when he arrived the message was gone. He'd stopped to rest, he'd rolled a cigarette, and he'd smoked the message. Loud, sad laughter, and then more stories about Bitlis—about Turks and Kurds, and the long dead among the Saroyans, Krikorians, Bazoyans, Melikians, Garoghlanians, and others. I used to listen from the adjoining room, but pretty soon I'd hear nailing in the backyard. That would be my brother Henry. I'd go out there and he'd be nailing together pieces to box-wood from Setrakian's packing-house: every which way, like a lot of sculpture these days.

"What are you making, Henry?"

"Nothing."

He'd throw the work of art over the barn. "Let's go out to Thompson ditch and swim."

So we'd go. Four miles. Unless we happened to run into a good ball game at California Field—or soccer, or football. We weren't allowed to go to the movies on Sundays. This had nothing to do with religion. It just didn't seem intelligent to leave the sunlight and go into a big dark room and sit.

When I was a messenger at Postal Telegraph, from my thirteenth to my fifteenth year, I tried to get Sunday overtime. First, because I preferred working, liked to listen to the telegraphers, and liked to sit at a typewriter and write. And second, because I could use the extra three dollars. My favorite character was old Davenport, the wire chief. He must have been seventy. He also must have been something like Mencken in the matter of religion. On the one hand, he scoffed at the church and churchgoers. On the other, all day Sunday he sang hymns and preached, chewing tobacco and chuckling.

What I'm forgetting, though, is the sense of slowness on Sundays. The boredom. The desperation. The feeling of being involved in dead time.

One Sunday afternoon when I was nine or ten my cousin Zav came over and complained that he was going mad.

"Let's go to Zapp's Park," he said.

This was a defunct amusement park out Blackstone Avenue, about three miles from our neighborhood. We walked it, and wandered around in the place, with the big irrigation ditch called Fancher Creek running through it, swift and silent. There was a little side ditch running into the main ditch. Zav jumped across this ditch. I decided to pole-vault across on the heavy eucalyptus branch I had found. The vault was unsuccessful, I fell into the water, and was carried out quickly to the center of the big stream, while Zav ran along, laughing his head off. It wasn't until I had been carried at least a hundred yards that I finally managed to get to the opposite side of the ditch and climb out, with Zav still laughing.

I said, "Why didn't you help me?"

He said, "How?"

"I might have drowned."

"Well, you didn't."

We got out of the shade of the trees that grew along the ditch bank, into the sun, and went on wandering around, so I'd be dry by the time I got home. We agreed not to mention the episode, because my mother would have clobbered me, since every summer the rivers and ditches of Fresno took the lives of two or three dozen small boys. Almost every day an item appeared in *The Fresno Eve-*

ning Herald, with a photograph of the boy, and my mother used to look at it and say, "Opsoss." (Alas.)

I find Sundays excellent for work—for the accelerating of work in progress, or for the starting and finishing of shorter works. Like old Davenport, I enjoy the Sunday stuff on the radio—all religions: Mormons, Jews, Catholics, Protestants, Christian Scientists. I especially enjoy the late Sunday night sermons and singing of Negro Baptists. Unlike old Davenport, or perhaps like him, I find it impossible to belittle the faith of anybody. On the contrary, I respect it deeply. I very much enjoy a wild, meaningless, emotional sermon. I don't much enjoy one that affects intelligence. It invariably seems spurious to me, as if a whirler had decided to put a few classical ballet movements into ecstasy.

Sunday is the day people go quietly mad, one way or another.

My Shoes
A Short Story From 1933

My Shoes: A Short Story From 1933 already has a note especially written for the appearance of the short story in June 1954 in *The Armenian Review*, Boston, so here I am now, in February 1968, writing still another note.

This is one of the short stories I wrote during my long apprenticeship. The story had a style that was not natural for me. That is the purpose of an apprenticeship, of course: it permits a writer to learn what he can do and what he can't. It compels him to discover his own style, or to discover that he has none, and must therefore be obliged either to give up writing or be satisfied to write in a skilled, competent but undistinguished way. The story is almost literally true. During the time of the apprenticeship which coincided with what I later learned had been the Depression I had to make my own way. Hence, I was forever looking for work, and so I went to a lot of places and met a lot of people in San Francisco—I certainly knew all of the people at the employment agencies. Every day I walked from 348 Carl Street to town, around town, to the Public Library, and then back. Shoes had always been important to me, as I suspect they always are to everybody. My Shoes didn't get me started as a writer. I sent it to a magazine, got it back, and put it aside. But it was part of the writing I did during the year 1933 that finally constituted the conclusion of my apprenticeship.

NOTE, 1954

In 1933 my writing had not yet appeared in a national magazine, but during that year I wrote many short stories, each of them experimental, because I hoped to find out from the writing of many kinds of stories which kind suited me best, only to discover in the end that I could not settle for any specific kind, as such.

Early in the year I began a long novel which I soon abandoned for two reasons: first, because the Armenian newspaper published in Boston, *Hairenik Daily,* which had invited me to be a contributor, was unable to bring out the novel in daily installments; and second, because quite frankly, I became bored with the whole idea, which was to trace the lives and fortunes of three kinds of Armenians, beginning in three different cities in Armenia and ending in three different cities in America: Markar, as I remember it, was a peasant-farmer who was transplanted (or transplanted himself) from the city of Moush to the city of Fresno; a merchant in Van became a merchant in New York; and a poet-preacher (my father) of Bitlis died an early death, amidst failure, poverty and sorrow, in San Francisco.

Novels that take eight or nine hundred pages in which to trace something or other are all right, I suppose, but I just couldn't be bothered in 1933.

During the month of October I wrote a novel to which I gave the high-flying title of *Trapeze Over the Universe,* out of which came, I should say, my first accepted short story, The Daring Young Man on the Flying Trapeze, which was written a few days after the novel had been finished.

I sent the story to the editors of *Story* Magazine, recently transferred from various places in Europe to New York. My note to the editors was belligerent. I dared them not to accept the story and still pretend they were interested in new writing and new writers. I had become fed up with rejection slips, or patronizing letters from idiot editors of insignificant magazines. I had decided late in 1932 not to send any more stories to any more editors, but to go on writing until I was thirty, at which time I planned to examine my work and decide if I wanted to continue in the profession.

The reason I broke my own rule was simple: I believed The Daring Young Man on the Flying Trapeze demonstrated that I was ready to begin my career in earnest.

Waiting for word from editors impels a kind of anxiety only unpublished writers know.

But then the whole business of wanting to be a writer is unique.

To begin with, the wish to write is not recognized by anybody as a real one with real possibilities. A man can decide to be a doctor, on the other hand, and he can go to school, and study, and meet all the requirements, and eventually become a doctor. And thereafter there is never an organized critical fraternity which reports publicly on the effectiveness or non-effectiveness of his work. Any doctor may make mistakes and continue to be a doctor, and even to enjoy the protection of his fellow professionals.

There is no formal procedure to the business of becoming a writer. There is no such thing as going to school, turning out so much work, and then being taken in by a magazine or a publishing house, as a doctor is taken in by a hospital.

Thus, the first requirement for the would-be writer would appear to be a willingness to work very hard for ten or fifteen years, without any guarantee that all of the time and effort shall not have been in vain.

In short, the would-be writer must be impractical at the outset, and a very wild gambler.

This tends to increase his loneliness, to point up his isolation, and to make of him something at best midway between a harmless eccentric and a sorrowfully comic character.

After the age of twenty, society (one's family and friends, at any rate) expects a man to fit into a proper order of things, to find a place in an acceptable pattern, to work, to keep regular hours, and to be able to pay his way to a wife, a home, children, promotions, plans for retirement.

Nobody is willing to believe in the would-be writer's writing, least of all the experts. (The very term Rejection Slip is insulting. The text of each of them is painful for the would-be writer even to behold—for there is no point in reading it. It is meaningless.)

Nobody says of the would-be writer, "He is going to become a writer." It is assumed that he is *not,* and the assumption is powerful. The would-be writer must be a little crazy to dispute the assumption and to hold fast to the theory that even against such overwhelming odds he is in fact going to become a writer someday—and of course the sooner the better: perhaps tomorrow, perhaps the day after.

In any case, while I waited for word from the editors of *Story,* I did a great deal of walking all over San Francisco. I lived next door to the Polytechnic High School, about four miles from the heart of town. I am not going to go into the importance to the would-be writer of doing a lot of walking during his apprenticeship, because he never knows where he stands in his apprenticeship; and if he walks a lot it's not because he has reasoned that it is important for him to do so, but because he hasn't carfare.

My shoes were important to me. I needed them more than I needed anything else, except a place to sleep and something to eat.

I believe (although I am not sure) that it was while I was waiting for word from the editors of *Story* that I lived and wrote My

Shoes, which is a deliberately facetious story about an unpublished writer.

Now, it goes without saying that the material could have been worked into another kind of story entirely, but this happens to be the story into which the material came together.

At last, a few days before Christmas, I saw the mailman come up Carl Street, stop at my door, and drop something in the mailbox. Among the mail I found a letter from the editors of *Story*. Yes, they wanted the story. Furthermore, they said I could expect a check for $15 sometime soon. It would be difficult—certainly time-taking—to make known now what this meant to me then, so I shall only say that if I had been a little mad before the letter arrived I went clean off my nut after it did, only now there seemed to be a little quality to my madness.

I was both pleased and unimpressed by this new circumstance in my career as a writer.

I began to make plans for the immediate future, and for the practical use of the fifteen dollars. When the money reached me I spent eleven dollars for an overcoat, and the rest of the money went for paper, envelopes, paper clips, and postage stamps.

My Shoes is not a lost and found masterpiece by an unpublished writer who, as luck would have it, turned out to be great. If anything, I was probably as great when I was unpublished as I shall ever be.

Shoes are still very important in my life. I now have half a dozen pairs, including a brand new pair in a box where they have already remained six years, but I still stay with a particular pair until it is virtually unwearable. I also polish all of my shoes myself—because I can do a better job than a bootblack, and because the business of polishing my shoes satisfies my soul.

I walk on my feet, and my feet are put into shoes whenever I am ready to walk, that's all.

MY SHOES, 1933

The job of writing a novel while a writer's feet are in worn-out shoes is difficult, as such a circumstance not only affects his circulation, but also his style. A good pair of shoes establishes a security between a writer and the world that is most desirable.

It is unfortunate therefore that my only pair of shoes has approximated, from long walking, a state very near total disintegration: the ball of each foot is exposed, so that on all my walks I go partly barefooted, and in the heart of town where lighted cigarettes fall thickest I may be seen almost any day leaping suddenly; as in church I dare not cross my legs. That is the price I pay (and gladly) for the honor of being a great, if unknown, writer.

The novel I am writing moves forward slowly; a paragraph a day, sometimes a single sentence, and not rarely only one word. Yesterday the word was cold, and so was the climate. (I address myself for the remainder of this paragraph to those who only read and do not know—cannot imagine—the daily ordeal of an honest writer: to you, ladies, and to you, gentlemen, and to all of my cousins, my daily production may seem meager, but I am prepared to offer a polite explanation to the ladies and gentlemen, and to swear at my cousins: I take pride in the enormous amount of bad writing I have had the skill not to put to paper. Furthermore, my integrity is sustained by the fact that although I have been writing for almost ten years I am not responsible for one bad novel. It is a pity, in my opinion, that no prize exists for the writer who best refrains from adding to the world's bad books.)

How have I managed this marvelous achievement?

Well, it is quite simple.

Until I am sure that I am ready to write greatly, I don't write at all. I walk.

For such a technique it is better to own a pair of good shoes than a typewriter, although two pairs would be better.

And so, in my life, walking is a very important business. As I walk on my own two feet, vanity, ambition, and other absurdities fall away from me, and I view the world with the clear eye of art, truth, wit, and humility.

My plans as I walked to town this morning were precise and pleasant: I would enter a shoe shop and have my worn-out shoes repaired.

At the first shop I was amazed to learn (since I had been able to borrow only a dollar and a half from my brother Henry) that the cost for the repairs would be a dollar and seventy cents, ten cents additional for sewing.

"I will return this evening," I said. "I am late for work."

At several other shops the cost proved very nearly the same, now a bit less, now a bit more.

All morning, on top of everything else, I hadn't had a cigarette, and I needed one badly.

At last I found a shop that advertised a rate for repairs that I could afford: sixty-five cents for half-soles, thirty-five for heels, and, the clerk said, twenty-five cents to take care of the rips, since there were five of them. This came to a total of a dollar and a quarter, leaving enough to cover the cost of a pack of cigarettes and seventy sheets of writing paper from Woolworth's.

I felt grateful, and immediately removed my shoes.

"To avail yourself of these bargain prices," the clerk said, "it is necessary to leave your shoes at our shop twenty-four hours. There is an additional charge for work done while you wait."

"How much will it cost to have the work done immediately?"

"A dollar and sixty cents."

I put on my shoes and said I would return later. I walked home, and tried on a pair of my brother Henry's discarded shoes. They were out of shape, in worse condition than my own, and too small, but I decided they would do until my own shoes were repaired.

I walked four miles slowly and painfully back to the shop, and the clerk announced that my shoes would be ready to wear the same hour the next day. He handed me a slip of paper with my name written on it.

"Shall I pay now or tomorrow?"

"Tomorrow."

It was now two o'clock in the afternoon, and since I had not yet smoked a cigarette I bought a pack and smoked one, then another, and another, so that in half an hour two fingers of my right hand were stained, and the corner of my mouth was scorched.

It was difficult to walk in Henry's shoes, so I went to the Public Library to sit down. I took Chekhov's *Letters* to a table in the Great Reading Room. A pretty girl sat at the table across from me, and there went the letters right out the window. In an hour I read forty pages without understanding a word.

When the girl got up to go, I remembered that I needed a breath of fresh air myself. In the hallway she opened her handbag, and from it fell a slip of paper, which I picked up quickly and handed to her. On the slip of paper was written: two cans tomato sauce, two bars soap, one box matches.

"Are you a stranger here?" I said.

"No," the girl said. "I was born in San Francisco."

"I'm a stranger here," I said.

"Oh," the girl said. "Where are you from?"

"Russia. I've been here only four years. I've been living in New York."

"You speak good English."

"My father was English. He was a mechanic in Moscow. My mother was Polish. Are you Spanish?"

"No. Roumanian."

"Well, it's practically the same thing."

We left the building and walked across the street to the Civic Center Park. An old man stood near the fountain feeding pigeons crumbled pieces of stale bread. He tossed the crumbs to the birds with the gesture of one sowing wheat.

We took a bench and watched the man. I began to smoke cigarettes quickly.

"My name is Charles Dilkins," I said. "What is yours?"

"Ester Bercovitz."

"Yes, that's Bulgarian. You look Spanish all right."

"Roumanian."

"Well, it's all the same. What were you reading at the library? I'm a writer."

"Are you, really?"

"Yes. I use a pen-name. You've probably read some of my stories.

"Are you *really* a writer?"

"Yes, of course. I'm working on a novel now."

"What name do you write under? Maybe I *have* read one of your books. I do a lot of reading. But you don't look like a writer."

"I know. I look more like a reader."

"What name do you use?"

"Sherwood Anderson."

"Are *you* Sherwood Anderson?"

"That's one of my pen-names. I have several others."

"I've *heard* of you all right, but I'm afraid I've never read any of your books."

"That's all right. I'll dedicate my next novel to you."

"That's very kind of you."

"Not at all. I was looking for somebody suitable to dedicate it to anyway."

"But you hardly know me."

"I know you well enough. A writer knows more about people than they do themselves. You'll like my novel."

"What's it called?"

"The Merry Money of Beggars."

"Oh, you are a writer!"

I lit another cigarette quickly.

"The novel is about a young man who has no money. In order to write about such a young man it is necessary for me to live the part. I have all the money I need, but I must pretend to be poor while I'm writing the novel."

"Is that the way books are written?"

"Yes."

"Do you make a lot of money writing?"

"I have a Cadillac."

"I thought all young writers are poor."

"They used to be, but these days they're not. Last year a friend of mine showed a net profit of fifty-seven thousand dollars."

"He must have done a lot of writing. When do you writers *find* the time to write so much?"

"It's easy. A writer is *always* on the job. His hours are *all* hours."

"I didn't know *that.*"

"Last Christmas, for instance, when the rest of the world was happy, I sat in my room working on a story called Joy to the World. And what did I get for it?"

"What?"

"Influenza."

"Did you have a fever?"

"One hundred and four, but I got a good story out of the fever, too. Did you know that during the two weeks in which Voltaire was ill with typhoid he wrote an opera, six essays denouncing Catholicism, four against the French government, a six-act play, and seventy-two letters?"

"No, I didn't."

"Now, in the novel I'm writing, the young man who has no money meets a beautiful girl in an art gallery. They take a fancy to one another."

"They do?"

"Yes. Would you like to see a movie?"

"All right," the girl said, so we got up and walked together to the Golden Gate Theatre on Market Street.

Matinee admission was thirty-five cents each.

We entered the great cathedral of darkness and secrecy on tiptoe.

Movies are all right, I guess, but it's the comfort of the plush seats that I cherish most, and I was pleased to sink contentedly beside my companion with not the faintest regret that the recovery of my shoes was now an uncertainty of the future. Tomorrow if I wished to walk to the zoo it would have to be in Henry's tight shoes, but no matter. One thing at a time is a good policy.

"Now they're married," the girl said suddenly.

"Who?"

"Martin and Helen Hayes."

"Who's Martin?"

"Ronald Colman."

"What picture is this?"

"Arrowsmith, from the novel of the same name by Sinclair Lewis."

I sat up and watched carefully.

"A nice picture," I whispered at the end.

"Yes," the girl said. "But she died, and I don't see why they couldn't let her live."

"Live and let live. On the other hand, life *is* sad."

The vaudeville overture fortunately silenced us. It was a medley of classical compositions by Irving Berlin, Walter Donaldson, Jimmy Monaco, Lew Pollack, and Franz Schubert. Next a curtain was parted, another raised, and the first act of the stage show began.

After the show we went to a restaurant.

"Eat all you like," I said.

"I'm glad I'm helping you with your novel," the girl said.

"It's a pleasure to be helped by *you*."

"I love children. Do you?"

"Yes."

I escorted the girl to her home, and then, since I no longer had the price of a streetcar ride, I began the long walk home. When I got there it was a few minutes after eight and I found my brother Henry sitting in my room pretending to be reading Ouspensky's *Tertium Organum*. He was beginning to nod from having been up since six in the morning to get to his job at Postal Telegraph.

"It says here," Henry said, "if rationality exists in the world, then it must permeate everything, although manifesting itself variously,' What does that mean?"

"The hell with it," I said. "I've been talking all afternoon, and enough's enough. Any mail for me?"

"Yes. This bill."

I dropped the bill in the wastebasket and removed Henry's shoes.

"Where'd you find *those* shoes?"

"Henry," I said, "my shoes are at the shoemaker's, and I've spent the dollar and a half I borrowed from you this morning."

"What for?"

"I met a pretty girl."

"Just a millionaire on the loose, is that it?"

"Yes. I began telling lies and showing off, and couldn't stop until the money was all gone. I told her I was Sherwood Anderson, I took her to a movie, and then to a restaurant. Now I'm broke."

"Who's Sherwood Anderson?"

"He's a writer, too."

"Is she a nice girl?"

"Yes, she is."

"I wish you'd write a best-seller," Henry said, "so you could live like a millionaire *all* the time."

"So do I."

"Well," Henry said, "I can't lend you any more money unless I inherit some money from somebody."

"I certainly hope you do."

Henry went to bed, and I sat down to work on my novel.

For two hours I worked very hard and wrote two sentences.

I then opened the windows of my room, and prayed.

"Our Father, if I have been a fool all day, it has been to Thy glory. If I have uttered one lie after another, it has been for Thy Amusement. Lord, there are enough who groan lamentations, which I presume must bore you. I have no gift for it. I cannot worship except with a joyous heart. Although I am ill-clothed, although my stomach groans from fasting, and my body shivers with cold, I praise Thy name. Thy kingdom come: there is no better school of writing."

Hushed by the enormity of space, the endlessness of time, and grateful to God for the solemnity of the night, and the benediction of sleep, I went to bed. But in the midst of sleep I sat up with a start to write down one last idea: "Write a story about your shoes."

Yesterday, Today, and Tomorrow

Yesterday, Today, and Tomorrow is a fragment about time, written in 1951 or 1952, and never sent anywhere.

If it were useful to decide about such words as yesterday, today, and tomorrow, and their meanings, and how they affect us, I suppose we might say that no word is so laden over with dignified sorrow and regret as yesterday, no word so filled with hope as well as anxiety as tomorrow, and none so confusing and contradictory as today.

The probable emotion accompanying each word might be best and quickest approximated by an exclamation: *Oh, yesterday. Ah, tomorrow. Alas, today.* Although it might also be, *Hurrah, today,* depending upon the nature of recent yesterdays and the prospect of approaching tomorrows, not to mention the nature of the individual involved. In any case, while the exclamations are interchangeable, it isn't easy to believe a poet will come along who will say, *Hurrah, yesterday.* (I for one wish he would, though, for I have no scorn for the past.)

Yesterday is supposed to be gone forever the minute it's gone, but the fact is that it stands at the very center of today. Yesterday is never gone, just as tomorrow is always here. The difficulty is always today—now—this minute.

What *is* today?

Everybody knows the story of the farmer's boy of ten or eleven who wanted to become very strong, and hit upon a scheme by which to achieve that condition. His father gave him a bull calf which the boy decided to lift in his arms every morning until it was full-grown.

I don't remember how the story turned out, but I know a full-grown bull is a very large and heavy commodity, and nothing for a full-grown man to try to lift, let alone a growing boy. Still, the boy's project has always appealed to me. What he meant to do with the bull, every man certainly means to do with time—one day at a time, but just as the bull soon grows beyond the grasp and strength of the boy, so does time—dozens of todays one after another, and then hundreds, and then thousands—three thousand six hundred and fifty of them, more or less, to every decade—certainly too many to cope with systematically.

In the end, today is forever, yesterday is still today, and tomorrow is already today.

Anybody Home?

Anybody Home? was written in 1954 for a manufacturer's give-away monthly pamphlet called *Perfect Home*. On the inside cover of each issue was a photograph of somebody with a name, and his definition of home. And so it came to pass that I was invited to send in my definition—for perhaps $100, but I'm not sure about that. Maybe it was for free. I received the pamphlet in the mail every month for two or three years, at any rate.

I don't know what home means to me, but then I don't know what anybody means by home. Home is the world, to begin with. A man reaches home when he's born. Home is also a man's nation, his native city, his neighborhood, and finally his house, his room, his table and chair and bed. That's geographical, but there are other aspects to the matter. Home is a man's family, which first of all is the human family. A man finds himself one among many. Home is also his nationality—American, Mexican, English, French, Italian or something else. Home is also a man's own father and mother or the memory of them, and his own son and daughter. There is still another aspect to the matter, and this aspect is cultural, which embraces the whole order of ideas. A man's home is intelligence, for instance, or fear or hatred of it. It is love of truth, honor, virtue, integrity, beauty, meaning, or unawareness of these things, or disrespect for them, depending on the man. Now, when home is a house, the matter becomes quite simple but at the same time con-

34

fusing. A house can be quite simply a place to eat, and sleep; or it can be a school from which the only graduation is death itself; a church in which humility, love, and truth are pursued until they are captured or the pursuer is; a library, an art gallery, a scientific laboratory, a studio in which in addition to other things a man's own meaning is made.

A man is himself his home, I suppose, and that's the reason it's not a simple thing to talk about. A home should mean everything, increasingly so all the time. The only real address I have ever had was my shoes, and I think that's the reason I have always had to stop at shoe stores to look at the shoes in the window. To become too devoted to a house, I think, is a profound mistake, or the beginning of commonplace failure. And yet the longing for a final house is great in all men, it seems. I know I began to long for my own home before I was nine years old, and my own son, at ten, has a whole lore of his own home—what a place, what a life, what fun, what ideas, what freedom, what intelligence, what wonders when he gets there. Will he make it? Will he ever for as long as a year, even, make it? Perhaps not, but in the meantime he's got his feet in his shoes, the sidewalk under his shoes, the world all around and that's where he is and where he lives, and in the end his only home. If we want our fathers and mothers and sons and daughters to live in a home that makes sense, all we have to do is make sense of the world itself. That's difficult, but we won't be apt to reach anything like a real home until we do make that kind of sense, or hit upon a means by which to believe we can eventually make that kind of sense.

All the same I still long for my own wonderful home, by which I mean a house in a proper place—but what am I talking about? I've been there from the beginning. I must be talking about heaven, like the singer in the revivalist song: "Oh, Lord, you know I have no friend like you. If heaven's not my home, oh, Lord, what shall I do?" (You shall live in the world, rather homeless, that's all.)

Remember the Joyride?

Remember the Joyride? was written in 1961 and sent to a number of editors who didn't care for it. I like it just the same. I'm interested in the stuff of which it is made: travel, memory, ego, and mistakes. During the first world war and immediately afterwards, in the early years of the automobile explosion, driving an automobile was a very special thing, closely connected with a man's eminence, wealth, personality, pride, and power. A man driving a car was a man of sex, so to put it. Taking a girl for a ride involved great speed and swift braking around a corner, during which the girl would be thrown against the driver, screaming happily, and the ice would be broken, as the psychiatric term for the banishment of fear or frigidity might be put.

On a drive from Oslo to Kristiansund in the month of May, 1961, an accident took place: I believed I was driving in California in 1941.

This interior accident—an accident of person, time, and place —puzzled me, because there was no satisfactory explanation for it. For longer than an hour I simply forgot that I was driving in Norway. The watery landscape, the woods and rocks, the highway signs, the towns and villages were unlike anything I had seen in California in 1941.

I must be homesick, I reasoned. And yet I felt entirely at home: in my car, the radio on, rolling easily along a winding, rising and falling highway, at peace with the world, the hunger of the eye satisfied every instant by good things to see: rock, foliage, flower, water, horse, cow, dog, man, woman, child, vista, sky, cloud, brook, river, lake, bay.

"So why did I feel I was in California twenty years ago?" I wondered.

There was no answer. The event was an accident, pure and simple, one of those pleasant little accidents one smiles about and forgets immediately. I couldn't forget it, though. I didn't want to, I suppose. I cherished it. I wanted to try to guess about it, and about motoring in general. The word *transport* has been used by poets who have been concerned about events of the spirit. I wondered if the act of motoring might not be considered to be such an event, in addition to an event of actual physical departure and arrival. Are motorists poets, whether they know it or not? Mute poets, who behold, feel, breathe, and experience a poetic mystique of being, simply because they are in fact going?

My destination for the day was Kristiansund, to which I came at length, in which I put aside the car and began to move about on foot. From seven to eleven in the evening I walked and came to places and stopped to sit and drink and remember other drives I had taken.

One of the best was the first of my life, from 3204 El Monte Way in Fresno in a Model T Ford north 200 miles to San Francisco, my brother Henry at the wheel.

Climbing Pacheco Pass the car moved so slowly that a quick-moving man on foot might have overtaken and passed us, but my brother refused to stop or even to believe the grade of the highway would *force us* to stop—and perhaps turn back. *That* we simply refused to think of doing. We were on our way to San Francisco and we would *get* to San Francisco.

At the summit my brother turned to me, smiled, nodded, and roared, "There. The Top. And now we *roll.*" And roll we did.

As luck would have it, at the bottom of the Pass we came to rain so heavy it was scarcely possible to think of it as rain at all. The black canvas top of the car was sopping wet, the visibility through the windshield was zero, and the highway was so slippery we were again afraid we would have to stop. The rain was a test, not only of the car, but of us. And then suddenly the rain stopped, and again my brother smiled, nodded, and roared, "San Francisco, here we come."

We weren't exactly kids—I was sixteen—but we weren't exactly veterans, either. And this *was* our first trip. If it flopped, there would be an unfortunate precedent that had to do not only with motoring, but with *going* in general. And we knew that to grow is to go. None of this was put into so many words, although we talked fairly steadily the whole nine or ten hours of the trip, which had begun a little before daybreak.

Family opposition to the trip had been reasonable, courteous, and intelligent, but in the end we not only won the dispute, we transformed the opposition into allies: a whole apple-box was filled with all kinds of good food to eat, surely enough for a week, in case the journey came to an unexpected end in a place where help might not be instantaneous.

It didn't, though, and we arrived in San Francisco safe and sound, exhilarated and proud.

Another good achievement of motoring I remembered during the visit to Kristiansund involved a secondhand Packard I bought in 1935 for $100 cash. This was a dashing-looking convertible I knew was on its last legs but wanted to have just the same. The motor had a condition. After a sudden stop, it could not be started again until it had cooled. This might take anywhere from five to fifteen minutes.

The car was bought in San Francisco and driven to Fresno by way of the same old Pacheco Pass, which it climbed like nothing.

I was twenty-seven then and had had one book published. The car seemed to suit a new American writer. After two days in the old home town, visiting friends and relatives, I took off for Los Angeles, so I could show the car to other friends. Midway in the journey, in the heart of Bakersfield, the car stopped at a traffic light when the evening traffic was heaviest. I expected a ticket from the cop who was urging me to move along. Instead, however, he began to motion to the motorists to come around the stalled car, which they did in good grace, only glancing at the chariot as if it couldn't possibly be true that something so magnificent could be flawed.

"Vapor lock?" the cop said.

"Yes. Shall we push it out of the way?"

"No, let it cool off, and then *drive* it away."

A small crowd gathered, apparently to admire the car, but who can really guess why crowds gather? They seem to *like* to gather, and are only waiting for the merest excuse to do so. The memorable thing about this crowd was the sudden arrival of an old lady. She didn't study the car, she studied me. I believed she might very well be somebody I had once known: one of my teachers at Emerson School, for instance. I gathered that she meant to speak to me in a moment, and I was rather pleased that she remembered me—the worst pupil at Emerson School, but for all that a man who had become a writer and the owner of a stalled Packard convertible. She fixed her eyes on mine, and then said, "Are you—?"

"Yes, I am."

I meant of course that I was the new American writer, whose name was already well known.

"John Muggerditchian!" the old lady said happily. "Do you remember your teacher, Miss Hollingberry, at Hanford High?"

"Of course, Miss Hollingberry," I said.

The cop said, "Want to give her a try now?"

I got back into the car, pressed the starter button, the motor fired, and so I was now only required to wave good-bye to the old lady.

I kept the Packard quite a long time, all things considered: about a year, and then I gave it to a cousin who understood vapor-lock and what to do about it.

Driving in Kristiansund I remembered other adventures of motoring, but in the end all of the motoring I had ever done gathered together into one long continuing trip—the trip of myself in the living world, high-rolling down the living highway to Bakersfield, Mexico City, Kristiansund, and meaning.

Money, Money, Money, and You Can Have It

Money, Money, Money, and You Can Have It was written in Malibu, in 1953, but never offered to an editor. I probably had in mind sending it to an editor, and then either misplaced the manuscript or decided not to bother because I didn't urgently need any money.

I want to write about the things I am glad to do without.

I do not have a television set. I do not subscribe to a newspaper. I do not buy books. I do not go to the theatre, or to movies. I do not buy new clothes.

I do not hire a housecleaner.

I do not hire a cook.

Those are some of the things I do without.

What do I do *with*? Well, I hear music every day—over the radio. I write every day. I read every day—magazines and books, for the most part, although I pick up *The Christian Science Monitor* free of charge from racks here and there now and then and glance through old issues. I eat every day. I sleep every day. I have a fire in the fireplace every day, but I do not buy logs. I burn driftwood.

Now, the minute I began to make my way in the world as a writer, I began to travel. I had money in my pocket, so I went around spending it as quickly as I could. When the money ran out, I sat down and worked half a day, or a week, and pretty soon there was so much more money to spend that I would have to run out as quickly as possible and get to work on it. But if I didn't feel like earning money by working, I would make a bet on a horse, and sure enough, my horse would win, and again I would have a lot of money to spend.

For years I was very lucky.

For instance, let's say I bet one hundred dollars on a horse, and it ran out of the money. Well, then, I bet two hundred dollars on another horse, and sure enough, this horse would win. Sometimes, I would have to bet four or five horses in order to get a winner, but I always got one, and I got the money I wanted.

I went to bed late and got up any time I felt like it. I ordered breakfast, and by the time I was out of the shower the waiter would be at the door with a table on wheels, with a fine white tablecloth spread over it, fine silver, fine china, and all kinds of good food to eat. I liked a broiled steak with O'Brien potatoes and watercress, but sometimes I had fish with lyonnaise potatoes, or broiled calf's liver with french fried onion rings, or baked lamb kidneys, or ham and eggs, or a cheese omelet. With the food the waiter always brought a copy of the morning paper and a pack of cigarettes.

Hardly a day went by that I didn't buy a new shirt, a new pair of shoes, or a new suit.

It was fun, and that brings me to the point I want to make.

It's just as much fun *not* to have money as it is to have money. It's just as much fun to do without as it is to do with. It's a luxury, in fact, to do without most things, and I expect to get rid of a few more as soon as possible. One of these days I am going to turn off the radio and leave it off for a year. What do I need with music? I've heard it all twice, anyway, most of it a hundred times. What do I need with the news, either? It's always the same. I look forward, also, to looking at fewer and fewer books, until at last I shall be satisfied to glance now and then at only one or two: the telephone directory, or the Armenian-English dictionary from Mesrob Kouyoumdjian in Cairo, published by the Sahag-Mesrob Press.

I'm not talking about poverty. Poverty is not having but wanting. Wealth is having and not wanting. Great wealth is neither having nor wanting. The greatest wealth of all is having so little that one must notice how much one has in having life itself.

The Small Rain

The Small Rain is what might be called a skit—neither story nor essay nor play, but with something of each in it. It is also from Malibu in the early 1950s.

No news has ever surpassed the weather in universal and everlasting appeal. (That means the weather has always been interesting to everybody.)

The first book of the Bible is full of the weather. There has never been an instant of time that hasn't had weather of some kind in it.

Plays, novels, stories, and poems count on the weather for much of their effectiveness.

Rain is a favorite kind of weather for both the very best and the very worst writers. Writers of movie stories use rain the minute they run out of ideas. It's nice. It's wet.

On the whole the earth is fair and habitable, but no place is ever entirely free of bad weather, as it's inaccurately called. And of course even the best weather can suddenly seem bad.

This is because every human being has his own personal weather.

The other night on my way home in Malibu after a neighborhood poker game, I stopped at a little highway bar for a bottle of beer. Even though it was Saturday night, there was only one other drinker in the place, a man who has played bit parts in movies for thirty years, a total stranger to me.

"When'd you get back?" he said.

"I didn't go," I said.

"Why not?"

"I was there before."

"I thought you went."

"I did, but not lately."

"I don't go any more, either. Rains too much."

"The steam-heat bothers *me*."

"Give me a fire any day."

"I like a fire, too."

"My favorite is a church on fire," the actor said.

"Yes, they're very nice."

"You expect to go soon?"

"Just as soon as I finish this beer."

A little woman came out of the shadows and stood beside the bit-player.

"I'd like you to meet my wife," he said. "Honey, this is a friend of mine."

"How do you do?" I said. The little woman smiled, and took her husband's elbow.

"You said just one more," she said. "Let's go."

"I don't want to go to Kansas City," he said. "I can't stand the rain."

He got down off the stool, though, and they left the place, walking slowly through a patch of very bad weather.

A moment later I went out, and sure enough it *was* raining all of a sudden.

I understand that in the early days it rained once for three million years. That's a lot of rain.

Memories of 1956

Memories of 1956 was written on January 1, 1957 at Malibu, and I find it fascinating for the stuff in it that I long ago forgot, including Oomphala's Spinning Wheel by Engelbert Humperdinck, whose music lately has been at the top of the hit parade in the form of a very pleasant waltz. (A young singer who hadn't had any real success under his own name shot to fame and fortune under the name of Engelbert Humperdinck. That's show business, most likely.)

Remember Christmas?

Remember New Year's Day?

Remember Hound Dog? O Holy Night? Auld Lang Syne? Oomphala's Spinning Wheel?

Well, Christmas was a Tuesday to me, and so was New Year's Day, and Tuesdays are Tuesdays, that's all.

All the same I remember Santa Claus and Scrooge.

On television I saw three versions of *A Christmas Carol:* an old movie version, a live musical version, and a plain live version. It's as much a part of Christmas as the tree, but the fact is it is also a delightful, touching, and bad piece of writing. It's a grocery story. The path to meaning passes through the Super Market. The way to achieve meaning is to buy a goose. Don't insult the poor, give them a few pennies. Don't fire your groveling clerk, give him a small raise. It may prevent his youngest son from dying before he's ten, and the tears come rolling down the face, because he's such a cheerful little fellow, and food on the table means so much to him. It's a bad story. Everybody loves it. Its message is the same as Elvis': Don't Be Mean. But *was* Scrooge mean? I don't think *he* was.

With the New Year came a new national highway automobile race, noise, excitement, and celebration—with still more tears. People with nothing to celebrate celebrated, as always.

A man's birthday is his new year, not January 1st. It's also his Christmas, not December 25th.

O Holy Night is a truly great song, both in music and in words:

> Long lay the world in sin and error pining
> Until He appeared and the soul felt its worth

In sin and error the world may no longer *pine,* but sin and error are certainly not gone from the world. Why should they be? How could they be? But the soul *does* have a worth, whether it is felt or not. And its worth has nothing to do with nickels and dimes, geese or groceries, December 25th or January 1st, Tuesday last year, Wednesday next, or any deep-seated annual habit of hysteria. The churchmen of television fame, when they receive their awards, chant nonsense just as the honest hustlers mumble it shyly.

O Holy Night has beauty, just as Hound Dog has laughter, and that's something worth cherishing, too. It is fashionable for half-intellectuals to make sport of Elvis Presley. That's easy to do of anybody—if you want to go to the trouble, or if you dare. The fact is that Elvis Presley is a singer with a touch of genius. Perhaps next Christmas he will have an album of sacred songs, including O Holy Night, and if he does, his singing will be expert and excellent. On the radio I have heard his version of one of my old favorites: Old Shep, a sloppily sentimental ballad of a man and a dog. The lyrics are so bad they are delightful, but the warm, half-wailing, half-whining melody has real order and pattern.

It can't compare with Auld Lang Syne, though, but then that's one of the greatest songs of all time.

It certainly suited the pitiful year of 1956.

As for Oomphala's Spinning Wheel, I can't wait for it to be transformed into a rock 'n' roll number for some real nervous cats.

Ah Silence,
Ah Music,
Ah Shut Up

Ah Silence, Ah Music, Ah Shut Up was written in August 1954. I am always interested in people I am near, and when somebody I don't know writes to me I'm interested in him and whatever he's interested in, or involved in. When the editor of *High Fidelity* wrote to me in the early 1950s and told me about the magazine and wondered if I might be willing to write for it now and then, even though it didn't pay very much, I asked him to please send me some back issues, and to put my name on the subscription list. When the back issues arrived I examined them, and every month when the new issue arrived I examined it. But even before the back issues arrived I saw no reason not to write for the magazine. The editor had been good enough to invite me to do so, and he had made known that the payment wouldn't be much, I felt comfortable about the whole thing, and immediately wrote this piece, and sent it along. I felt good about it, as if I had earned my supper, as the hunter who goes out in the evening probably feels when he fetches home a pheasant. There was nothing big about any of it, nobody expected anything to revolutionize anything, and therefore the rewards in all dimensions were quiet and small. Almost unAmerican, one mght say. About ten years after I became a professional writer I decided not to give away any more of my writing to small magazines or special publications of any kind. I insisted on being paid, even if the sum paid was as little as $5, which was now and then all the magazine could, in fact, pay, and as recently as 1966 I wrote several pieces for which I received $10. If the worst comes to the worst, I make a swap—my piece for a free subscription to the magazine. Now and then, though, I feel I ought to go out of my way to write new stuff for little magazines that simply cannot pay anything at all—not even a dime. But somehow I don't. I suppose it's because doing that is something only a very young man can do naturally, or inevitably. And he is generally unpublished or even unpublishable and is giving away his writing in order to continue his apprenticeship, or to find out if he ought to forget it and get into another trade, profession, or way of life.

From the time I wake up in the morning to the time I go to sleep at night I listen to music on the radio.

Perhaps it would be more accurate to say that I overhear music, because for many years now everything I hear has been heard before, so that I am not required to listen. Another reason I overhear the music rather than hear it is that when I am awake I am at work, or I am thinking about work, or I am reading.

Is such a relationship to music useless?

No, it isn't. It's useful, as I shall explain in a moment.

First, though, there is the matter of sounds of *any* kind, of silence, and of hearing. These must all be taken into account.

Sounds, then.

I decided to live by the sea for a number of reasons, all of which I shall skip excepting the reason that I wanted to be near the sound of the sea. I like it. I like the apparent sameness of it, and I like the variety of it. The sea, or rather the action of the tide, is never entirely soundless, for instance, although it is frequently almost so, and yet the sound of it is frequently a statement of silence.

Now, it happens that I am devoted to silence, although one would suspect the contrary since I not only live by the sea but have the radio on all day and much of the night. I am devoted to silence just the same. Now and then this devotion keeps the radio shut for as long as a week, and once a year for a month. I can't turn off the sea, however, but the sea itself quiets down by regular pattern, by a lunar system I do not understand and have not studied, and when this is so there is a good deal of silence all around, which I cherish deeply.

But what is silence? Is there in fact any such thing? Silence is *relative* silence. There are as many kinds of silences as there are human beings with the ability or inability to hear, or to listen.

It happens that for thirty years my right ear has been better than half deaf. Anybody whose hearing is not first-rate must cultivate listening. Doing this impels a search for things worth listening to. Conversation seldom is, and that is the reason I do not ever expect to wear a hearing aid. What does a listener tend to listen for?

Most of all for clarity. Anybody who speaks clearly I can listen to with a certain amount of pleasure not connected with the words spoken or the meaning of them. Anybody who doesn't speak clearly I can't hear at all insofar as words and their probable meaning is concerned.

Thus, human speech itself becomes something like music or song. I overhear most speech, and I listen to a little. Speech that I overhear is a meaningless but not necessarily unpleasant jumble. Speech that I listen to is a meaningful but not necessarily pleasant clarity. I can listen carefully to anything and hear it, but not having good hearing I tend not to listen to anything that isn't worth the intellectual exercise of listening. This includes music.

Sounds made by the breath of human beings are varied: all the grades of laughter, for instance: all the sounds of enthusiasm or zest, all the sounds of weariness, boredom, or grief. Noblest of all, though, is the sound of human breath in proper speech, and after that in song. It is a pity therefore that only actors cultivate the art of speech, because when they are not acting they seldom have anything to say worth listening to.

Noise is often worth listening to. The noise of New York, for instance, ought to be listened to now and then, and not just overheard. It is frequently rewarding. This goes for any city or town, of course.

Music, then.

The presence of music in the midst of work is any or all of the following things: a companionship, an example of an evolved and completed work while I am trying to achieve a similar commonplace or miracle, a diversion which is deeply satisfying without making any demands on my concentration, a source of ideas.

It is also a number of other things, but perhaps best and most of all it is a useful reminder that the very greatest achievements of the mortal soul are commonplace, ignored, unheeded, and in a certain sense useless. The human soul pours forth in astonishing variety and richness, in the form and pattern, texture and rhythm, of a language named music—composed in anguish or joy, anger or love, by men who have been dead several hundred years, or by men who are presently dying. As the music is overheard or listened to, it is impossible for the listener not to hear a little music of his own.

Music is the natural, the inevitable, the proper companion of all human activity, whether it is the writing of poems or plays, or the making of cigars or automobile parts. It is a great comfort to cows as well, as it most certainly should be.

Earthly and Heavenly Voices

Earthly and Heavenly Voices was written for *High Fidelity* magazine in January 1955. The editor wanted to know what I thought of writers reading their stuff. Ambrose Bierce believed writers should never be seen or heard. He was the contemporary of writers who got rich being seen and heard on the lecture trail—Mark Twain, Joaquin Miller, Bret Harte, Josh Billings, and very nearly all of the other famous American writers of that time. Talking and reading was easy work and paid well, and it seemed to satisfy something a man so rare in spirit as Mark Twain did not believe was shabby. He welcomed the fame, fuss, applause, and money, just as lesser men whose profession is acting thrive on such things, and then go to pieces when they stop, as of course they must. Ambrose Bierce had no such hunger. Mark Twain claimed he despised the human race. Ambrose Bierce actually did. But having the voices of writers on records is a good idea. I certainly like to listen to the way they read their stuff, or talk, or breathe.

On long-playing records one may listen to Dylan Thomas, T. S. Eliot, Sean O'Casey, Gertrude Stein, Robert Benchley, Merrill Moore, E. E. Cummings, and quite a few others.

Does the making of such a record add to or detract from the total impression of a writer and his work?

I think the existence of such a record, or even a series of such records, does neither, strictly speaking. Reading will always be reading, and no reader hears a writer's voice when he reads, if in fact he hears any voice at all, excepting perhaps his own. Silent reading does not appear to be in danger of disappearing. The silence of it is much too attractive.

On the other hand, listening to writers on records may very well become as appealing as listening to anything else on records.

Writers' records will probably be kept available, as their books are kept available.

Should a writer permit his voice to be made available?

I think he should.

All writers, good and bad, tend to be difficult to account for. Having the voice of a writer to listen to is apt to be at least a little helpful—in case it is ever worth anybody's time to want to try to account for his achievement, or his failure.

If records of the voices of writers of the past were available, whom would I want to listen to? Well, I would especially like to hear the voices of Guy de Maupassant, Leo Tolstoy, Jack London, Mark Twain, Anton Chekhov, Charles Dickens, Goethe, Strindberg, Ibsen, Hamsun, Ambrose Bierce, Joaquin Miller, Maxim Gorky, Balzac, Walt Whitman, Poe, and O. Henry.

Most of the names I have mentioned belong to men who were alive when recordings of one sort or another *could* have been made.

In my opinion writers are more worth listening to than those we have always hardly ever been able not to listen to: who may be lumped together as those who have something to sell. Writers have either nothing to sell, or truth alone, which in the present market is very difficult to give away, even. But it can be done, and if anybody can do it writers can.

Me and My Big Gray Horse

Me and My Big Gray Horse was written in San Francisco on January 29, 1963, perhaps to send to somebody in connection with Library Week, although I am not sure about that. I know it was written suddenly, for no payment, at somebody's request, for a good cause, as the saying is. I have a fondness for being invited to do some kind of new writing on a small scale and then doing it immediately and getting it out of the way. It doesn't take long to understand that there is to be no payment, that the writing isn't going to make or break my name, and the subject is something I've been thinking about all my life, in any case, so what am I waiting for?

If everybody in the world is not a writer, everybody is certainly a character in a work of fiction. Everybody is himself, and a hero. How could he possibly be anything else? Every day of every man's life is crowded with the stuff of writing: other characters, and great numbers of strangers; routine events, and unexpected events; pleasures, and unpleasantnesses; jokes, and threats; delights, and dangers. The drama is continuous, and the hero is always heroic. He certainly survives, doesn't he? Well, in the heart of every man isn't that the truly great achievement of every day, every year, every decade, every lifetime? Finally, he is no longer able to survive, but by that time he has been heroic at least a million times and the event has begun to be a little repetitious. A writer has died. Or a major character in a great novel has died. Or a bit-player in a

51

tremendous play has died. Or an extra in an epic movie has died. Lawrence of Albany, perhaps.

Now, we may presume that all art has come to pass at least partly as a consequence of this basic truth or human condition: life starts and stops, people begin and end, all things change continuously, so how can a fellow be expected to understand anything when the next time he looks at it the thing is no longer what it had been? In short, since all is in motion, how do we arrest the motion, so that we may be able to have a good look at it?

One of the ways hit upon by good luck, accident and sheer stubborn determination was writing. The very theory of writing, of naming things and actions, almost in itself compelled a stoppage of the incessant motion. If one looked at a nameless animal and gave it the name horse, one had that animal roped and corralled forever. Naming an animal or thing makes it particular and in a sense everlasting. Horse. Gray horse. Big gray horse. My big gray horse. And in this manner literary art begins, because it has *got* to begin. Me and my big gray horse, we went out across the desert to the end of it and almost fell, and then came safely back with this message: don't go out there. And suddenly there was the amazing reality of the lie, the invented, the imagined, the pretended; the speculation, the guess, based upon fear of probability, hunch or imagination. The magnificent thing about the lie has always been that it provides man with something real and tangible to repudiate, to correct, to expose, to destroy—only nothing is more difficult to destroy than a good fat whopping lie. People love them and probably should. It keeps them important. It permits them to feel good —better than other people, for instance, or more refined than pigs, and with a skin color far better than green or purple. Any fat whopping lie will do very nicely because the hero is really a fairly pathetic character, and even after going to college is fairly stupid, and with so much going on all over the place in a kind of squirrel-cage manner fairly feeble and confused.

Perhaps as good a way as any for him to stop being pathetic, stupid, feeble and confused would be to become a writer—first, a writer of his name, again and again, until he had come to understand something about it, about himself, and about the multitudes in the world, also named. And then he might try writing his address, his full address, including World, Universe, Solar System, Enormity, Timeless, Spaceless, Boundless, and so on. After that, all he would need to do would be to write the details: Well, I was there. It was a hell of a place, and I made it great, me and my big gray horse, brain, mouth.

C,A,T Cat Spells Everything

C,A,T Cat Spells Everything was written in February 1957, and read as a talk at the University of Southern California, something I seldom do, and up to that time had never before done. I suspect most talking, and mistrust all oratory. If somebody says something, somebody else should be in a position to say something back. A writer being applauded after a talk has a good chance of developing into a bigger fool than he could ever be doing his proper work.

It is not impossible to imagine the human race without a language, but it *is* useless, for the very *weight* of books is greater now than the weight of cities. The Library is larger than the world. While it *is* possible for anybody who wishes to do so to stay in the light of the sun as he travels around the world before a full day has gone by, a visitor to the Library could not, even in a hundred years, pass through more than a small portion of the books.

There is still only one way to experience a book; you must read it.

If a novel such as *Huckleberry Finn,* for instance, is made into a movie, it is no longer a novel, it is a movie.

If a tone poem is given the name Leaves of Grass, it has no connection with anything Walt Whitman wrote.

If O. Henry's story, The Furnished Room, were the means by which a designer achieved an interesting roll of wallpaper, the wallpaper would be no more related to the story than if its theme had been red roses, cherry trees, hatchets, or the face of George Washington as it appears on currency.

A written thing is a written thing.

It must be read in order to be experienced.

In the beginning, the Word was not. The Thing was. The recognition of the thing was visual. The Thing was itself, and there was no mistake about it. A tree was a tree as long as it was a tree. It was not a word, spoken or written. An animal was an animal. The sun was the sun, as it still is, whatever its fable and meaning may be to different people in different places.

But things look like other things.

The sea draws pictures on stones, or washes stones into shapes that are not unlike the shapes of bird, animal and/or man. Clouds assume forms that seem familiar. The bark of a tree may contain a picture of a whole countryside. The wind moving through a tree makes a series of pictures. The fruit of a tree may resemble any number of other things. The face of a lion may seem not unlike the face of somebody's father. The eyes of a calf may seem as pure and trusting as those of somebody's small daughter.

Everything is specifically itself, but there is nothing that isn't like something else, if only another of its kind. At the same time, everything is at least a little unique and separate. A grain of sand and another grain of sand are not the same grain of sand.

The arrival in matter of the Eye may be presumed to be the beginning of the impulse toward the Word. With the Eye came Notice, and with Notice came Comparison and Memory, both of which need help, since things move so swiftly, change, disappear, die.

The flux of things, the action and change of them, their rise and decline, blossom and decay, start and stop, almost *demands* a means by which to arrest this motion, for purposes of comparison, respect, and study, to name only a few.

If a man killed a bear and wanted everybody to know that he had, he would need to make it clear that he killed a bear and not a beaver, and that it was himself and nobody else who had killed it. The easiest way to do that is to show the bear and its killer to others. But soon the flesh of the bear is eaten, the bones carved into tools, the skin made into clothing, the killer grows old, and dies. Who remembers that he killed a bear?

There is a sad, an aching need, for man to establish clearly who he is, and what he does. Man believes he is a kind of thing that has meaning, and perhaps even a relationship to something vast and secret and wonderful beyond conception.

Long ago man drew a picture. He made a symbol that stood for himself, and a great many other symbols that stood for other things. For each picture and symbol he had a sound which he could make on purpose. Soon he had a whole assortment of pictures and symbols, sounds and series of sounds.

He had the Word.

He had language, spoken and written.

With the Eye and with the Word he made everything, and he's still doing it, although nothing among Things themselves is very much different now than it ever was. He just notices more, and has more to say about everything. The sun, for instance, is still the sun, but the lore about it is now vast, and the relationship of the sun to everything else broadens and enlarges and grows more meaningful every year.

In my opinion, the Word came to pass because Man was both unwilling and unable to believe he was only what he appeared to be: that is, a form of living thing which came into being blindly. For some reason, Man had to have more—more of everything— and so he *made* more.

He made it with the Word.

Why he had to have more, I don't know, and I doubt if anybody else does, or ever has known, but it's certainly something to think about, as of course we've been doing for some time.

Man at his *best* had to have more: Man as Man, not as Animal. At less than his best, Man, even now, does not have to have more. What he has is enough. Great and good multitudes come and go, live and die without demanding, or making more. Such multitudes are constant, and they are not to be considered inferior, useless, or meaningless. At the most, they are to be recognized, insofar as even that is possible. To scorn the multitude, or regret it, would be the equivalent of the Eye scorning the Foot, for Man is Man, and all of him throughout all Mortal Time is One. The Eye sees on behalf of the Foot. The Founders of the Word, the Users of Language, the Measurers of Less and More, the Creators of Method and Meaning, have done what they have done, and do what they do, for All.

If few write, many read. If few read, many listen, and all speak. Whoever the writer of the Book of Genesis may have been, whatever he may have been thinking at the time, what he wrote belongs to the multitude, too, for good or bad, or a little of each. If it isn't altogether Gospel, neither is it entirely Gossip. It certainly isn't Science or History, both of which, though presently highly-esteemed, may one day be noticed to have been slightly less than Gospel and only slightly more than Gossip. What the Book of Genesis is is Art. It is Child's Art, even if the writer was an old man, with an old wife, and old children.

Before the Word, Man wanted more. After the Word, he wanted also to be Right, or Unmistaken. The Library of the world is full of his happy and sorrowful seeking after the truth.

As a writer, as one who loves the Word, who is delighted by its buoyant fluidity and angered by its unyielding hardness, I shall not pretend that the following account of my earliest association with the Word, with language, with writing, is common to other writers, or that the account means anything in particular. It means only a little. It's interesting to me. And this is an appropriate time to bring it up. It is Gospel in that it's true, and it's Gossip in that it doesn't especially matter that it is true.

I had the good luck of having good eyesight from the beginning. I enjoyed the ability to see, and I delighted in much that I saw. I understood nothing, but nothing hung in the balance on that account, and so it was considered to be enough that I was there, and out of pain.

I did not study and learn how to speak, but I spoke. English first, and later Armenian, a language never spoken by many, nowadays studied by almost none, and yet a very rich language, which at this moment is beside the point.

When the time came I was sent to public school. It was expected of me that I would soon learn the alphabet, and then that I would learn to read, and then to write.

As it turned out, this actually happened, but the point I want to make is that I remember as vividly as if it were something that was very real only this morning that I saw no reason why it was necessary for me (or for that matter anybody else) to learn to read and write.

I knew how to speak. I could hear. I could see. And I was getting along fine.

And there, all of a sudden, was something called the alphabet, and I was expected to understand and use it. I was expected to understand A, and to make something of it. And the same with B, C, D, and all the other letters of the alphabet.

Well, to me A was a picture, but I was bullied into believing that it was not a picture; it was A. And so it was with B. I looked at each of the pictures of each of the letters of the alphabet, and I knew which was which, as I knew the sound for each of them. And so I knew the alphabet.

What I couldn't understand was what good was it, since for years—from what I believed to be the beginning—I had been speaking anyway, without having known the alphabet, without in fact suspecting that speech had anything to do with anything else— without suspecting it had anything to do with words, even. I believed it had to do with me, with love, with family, with house, with world, with human life together. Wasn't that enough? It wasn't. My teacher at school said it wasn't. My mother said it wasn't. My brother said it wasn't. My sisters said it wasn't. My grandmother who spoke Armenian, Turkish, and Kurdish, but had never gone to school, and couldn't read or write any language, also said it wasn't.

I could breathe and walk and run and eat and sleep and speak and laugh and sing and play games and have fun, and think, so why did I have to read and write, too?

I hated the alphabet. I hated the Word. I hated language. I knew days, weeks, and months of angry paranoia. I believed unknown parties had devised a diabolic project by which to force me to learn something I didn't want to learn. I was satisfied to be illiterate, to live and look, while everybody else in my class learned to read and write as if it were nothing. One morning our teacher printed C, A, T on the blackboard and asked what the word was. Everybody said cat. I looked and I saw three pictures on the blackboard. Not one of the pictures, not all three of them together, even remotely resembled a cat. The house in which I lived had a cat. It was a fine cat. I had seen it with a captured mouse. I had both seen and heard it *eat* a mouse. A cat is alive. It has fur. It speaks, sometimes for a dish of milk, sometimes just to be speaking. It spreads out near the stove in the kitchen and sleeps. It wakes up, lifts its head, and looks around as if it were remembering something. It gets up on its feet, and it slowly stretches every muscle in its body. It keeps itself clean by licking its fur. It leaps onto your lap to be nearer than where it had been. What did C, A, T on the blackboard have to do with what I knew?

I considered the Word fraudulent. I believed it was a trick, a deception, a confounder, a liar, a cheat, an intimidation, a spoiler of reality, bunk and skullduggery. All the same, it *had* been established that it was necessary for me to learn to read and write.

I struggled with this problem bitterly. I lived my whole life *in thought* fully and creatively, *without* knowing how to read and write. I planted vines and trees and harvested grapes and figs. I made kites and flew them. I met family and friends and spoke with them, and loved them. I whittled things out of wood. I drew pictures on paper. I made things out of clay. I rode a bicycle back and forth. I looked at another who also hadn't learned to read and write and together we smiled at those who had. I had a house of my own, full of my own kids, who also didn't know how to read and write, and they were alive, sensible, and very interesting. In thought, I lived my whole life without learning to read and write.

Even now, I do not believe I couldn't have lived a full and creative life without knowing how to read and write. I could have, and there's no telling how much more I would have become, or how much more the world would have gained.

There is no connection, in other words, between being intelligent and creative and knowing how to read and write.

In time I got the hang of it. I learned to read and write. But I don't think we really know what learning is. I didn't *learn* to read and write. If I had learned, I would have been reading and writing when everybody else in my class had been doing so, instead of puzzling over the pictures and *pretending* to read, whereas in reality all I was doing was *saying* a whole page which as a *picture* I had come to know signified a series of spoken words. Reading and writing *came* to me. I learned *other things* while I was *supposed* to be learning to read and write. Some of the things I learned are still useful: looking at something *particularly*, for instance, including a word on a page. Looking at the thing itself, as itself, rather than as the symbol of something else.

My handwriting turned out to be the best not only in my own class, but in the whole school, named Emerson. My letter to Mayor Toomey inviting him to pay the school a visit was judged the best written by any pupil in the school. It was sent to him, and he paid the school a visit.

Before I was eight I began to sell *The Fresno Evening Herald* after school every day. The newsboys waited for their papers in the basement where the printing press was, and so I witnessed and heard the working of a press as it quickly manufactured hundreds of copies of one day's newspaper. The next day it was a different edition, with different news. I also sold *The Saturday Evening Post* every Thursday. At home I examined both the newspaper and the magazine, but the Word had not yet come alive for me. Things only were alive for me, still.

The Bible figured in the life of my family. I had heard that the Bible was the word of God, and so I believed God had written it. It didn't matter that I didn't have a very clear idea as to who or what God was. Without needing to have a clear idea, without needing to define God, I believed I knew who God was, and somewhere along the line I began to believe that not only had He written the Bible, He had written *all* books. I therefore believed the Word was God's.

I was rather well along in years before the obvious thrust aside the mythical, the marvelous, and in a sense the more deeply true, if superficially false. God, as such, wrote nothing as a matter of fact —not the Bible, not the dictionary, not any other book, not even the word cat. Men wrote. They wrote the Bible, the dictionary, the books, and cat. Boys, as such, didn't write the books, and for the most part they didn't read any of them, either.

I read around in *The Fresno Evening Herald* and *The Saturday Evening Post,* mainly because copies were always around.

Even so, the Word was still away out there somewhere, whether written or read. The book was still away out there. Language was still away out there. I was busy. When I wasn't running, I was sleeping. When I wasn't listening, I was thinking. What I wanted to know was, What does it mean? In the streets I saw the faces of many people, many kinds of people, in all kinds of weather, and under all kinds of circumstances. What did the people mean? What did I mean? What did the world mean?

I didn't know. I didn't know anybody who did. Or if they did, they weren't saying. Or couldn't. It was a silent thing. A glance, a half-smile, a slight nod, half a gesture. That wasn't enough. I needed to know. The earnest faces of the poor, and the spurious smiles of the secure—what did they mean? The voices of the anxious and troubled, the shouts of the angry, the cries of the hurt, the whinings of the pitiful, the weeping of the lost and lonely— what did these things mean?

Leaving the First Armenian Presbyterian Sunday School one morning I noticed three apple-boxes full of secondhand books on the floor of the hall and I was invited to take one. I did, and it was trash. It was called *Sink or Swim.* I read it straight through. It was about a boy who sold papers. Somewhere in the book he sat down and ate bread and butter he had bought with money he had earned.

The reading of *Sink or Swim* may very well have been the beginning of my life as a writer. If it wasn't, it certainly came very near the beginning. Now, of course, this beginning may be presumed to have been inevitable in any case if we're willing to take our chances here, and if it hadn't been *Sink or Swim,* it would have been another book—any other. I'm glad it was *Sink or Swim,* however—trash, that is. Let no one forget the power of *any* book in relation to the right reader at the right time. Let no book be scorned, since any book is certainly at least a part of the one book, as Donne said of men.

Still, the reading of *Sink or Swim* didn't bring me understanding, or send me to an examination of all of the books in the Public

Library. That was to come later, and again, strictly speaking, unaccountably or to put it another way, inevitably, as part of the unfolding of a whole identity.

I still didn't understand anything, but I was still looking, and still trying.

One day I began to read *Oliver Twist* by Charles Dickens. In the reading of that preposterous, painful, laughing, sorrowful, eccentric, half-mad, wonderful fable, the Word moved a little nearer to the center of my spirit, and if I still didn't have any answers, I had a broader order of questions.

Days, weeks, months, and years of watching, waiting, and expecting, and there suddenly in a little story called in English, The Bell, by Guy de Maupassant, I came upon something at last: pity. A village beggar with both legs gone swings on his crutches like a gong inside a bell, and so he is called The Bell. The great Frenchman who was himself so much of a child in spite of his superficial worldliness, and so much of a saint in spite of his involvement in what used to be known as sin, tells the story of the murder of the beggar by neglect, tells the story without taking sides, with an indifference even, that is soon a rage in the heart and tears in the eyes—not for the beggar, but for life itself, for the whole human race, for the denied and unfortunate, but also for the undenied and fortunate, since he and they are one.

I read this story sometime near the end of my career as a newsboy, a short time before I became a messenger. The immediate effect remained with me the whole afternoon and evening, as I sold papers. I felt that I had got it at last. This is what it was, and for all I know still is: There is no answer, as such. There is no meaning, as such. All of it must be noticed very carefully, very particularly, and then noticed again. It must be noticed with a clear eye, with love, and with pity.

That day the Word settled down in the center of my spirit. On and off, it has been there ever since.

Sink or Swim. Oliver Twist. A short story by Guy de Maupassant. And one by Jack London, which I read about the same time as I read the story by the Frenchman. Jack London's story was called War.

I was a writer from the beginning, I suppose, in spite of my childhood quarrel with the whole theory of language. The works I have just mentioned plunged me headlong into the working life of the writer, which begins, as I have said and must say again, with careful looking, continues with reading, and begins to be resolved by writing.

What is the purpose of the Word?

In my opinion, its purpose is to influence Man's behavior, nature, and identity for the better.

That is not unlike the purpose of the sun in shining on human life, but why should it be? And it doesn't matter that neither the sun nor the word are able to influence for the better *suddenly*.

I don't remember where I started, but this is where I stop, for a very simple reason. I want another try at it, at another time.

Armenia and Her
Po*t* Charentz

Armenia and Her Poet Charentz appeared in *Hairenik,* an Armenian weekly published in the English language in Boston, in June 1954. The word Hairenik means in the Armenian language Armenia, although Hayastan means the same thing, and Nairi almost the same thing, being an earlier name the Armenians had for their country. The word *yerkire* to an Armenian means unmistakably our country, our nation, our place, our meaning. It is impossible for the Armenian language to utter the sounds that constitute the word Armenia—there just isn't any such combination of sounds. There is, however, the name Armenak—my father's name—but this name arrived from outside the country, most likely, as several other names did, such as Zabel, pronounced softly, Zahpel, surely from the Iberian Isabelle.

In 1936 Yeghishe Charentz, not yet 40 years old, committed suicide in a jail cell in Erivan by ramming his head against a stone wall, or so the story goes. He had been a drug addict most of his life, but in jail his supply was cut off, and the story goes that his suffering became unbearable. One cannot be sure about such stories, but I know that he needed to ask me to step out onto the balcony of his hotel room in Moscow in 1935 while he gave himself a shot in the arm. A lot of great men in Russia were driven to the wall or stood up against it by the tensions, suspicions, fears, and poor mental health of the highest members of the Soviet government during its first three decades. Isaac Babel from Odessa, for instance—not even Maxim Gorky could protect him from the paranoid men who ran the show, and made a success of it, too, as we all know. (What we don't know, and perhaps can never be sure of, is that any other government might have made an even greater success of Russia and its people, at no cost at all in humanity, honor, truth, integrity, dignity, and the lives of its geniuses.) One cannot be sure Gorky himself was not finally eased out of his life and time.

Two things sent me to Armenia in the Spring of 1935 when I was twenty-six years old: a writer's restlessness, and a son's need to see his father's birthplace.

I took off, however, for a much simpler reason: I could afford to do so. By writing, by the sweat of my brow, I had at last earned both money enough to pay my way and the right to move about as I might see fit.

I had always found too many things wrong in the world, too much of man's nature mean, and too much of his life meaningless, to be at ease about my own life.

I had always been unimpressed by anybody I had ever met, although I had found many people amusing or kindly. The kindly man was generally weak, the amusing man almost invariably crooked.

In a way I suppose it was just as well that my father was dead, for it is not unlikely that I would have found fault with him, too. But since he was dead, I dwelt on his good qualities, and paid no attention to his bad ones: his inability to prosper in the world, to get along among commonplace men on their own terms, to take the world with a grain of salt, to make a joke of it.

In my boyhood I remembered my father as a good man, dead at the age of thirty-six, before I was three.

Nobody ever had a critical word to say of him, so that I myself in asking questions about his life and work tried to provoke criticism. In this I was unsuccessful. The worst that anybody was willing to say of him was that he was too good for this world. I accepted this theory with simultaneous admiration and disbelief, but I made up my mind to go back where he had come from as soon as possible.

My chance came at last after my first book had been published.

I took a train from San Francisco to New York, and a ship from New York to Europe.

I was not unaware that in reaching Soviet Armenia I would not be reaching my father's Armenia, or his city, Bitlis. It was enough at that time to reach the general vicinity of my father's birthplace, and to be in a nation named Armenia, inhabited by Armenians.

On my way south from Kiev to Kharkhov to Rostov to Ordzho-nikidze to Tiflis to Erivan a great expectancy filled my heart, as well as a great sorrow, as if I were on my way to the place where all of my family, and my father, had failed: his failure driving him to America at last, where, if anything, he became more out of place than ever.

As the train moved south, more and more Armenians came aboard. Just seeing and hearing them gave me pleasure.

Only one Armenian on the train was a political man. He was very old, and a famous philosopher of economy, who had taught at various universities, and had written books. But even this quiet-spoken man was not zealous about political theories. He was a man of culture, wit, and worldliness. While it had been expedient for him to investigate economic theories, it would be a mistake to believe that he cared more for one order of them than for another. He neither criticized nor praised the economic and political systems of Russia or of America.

I had to wait for a boy of eleven in the lobby of the New Erivan Hotel to point out to me the terrible flaws of the American economic and political system. I have frequently wondered about that boy. It is not unlikely that he is now one of the great men of Soviet Russia. I did not find him offensive, although excessively bright boys tend to annoy and irritate me. As a joke I asked him if he could play the violin and was delighted when he told me he had no time for such frivolity. My laughter did not move him to so much as a smile. He simply remarked that Americans were forever laugh-ing because of the contradictory nature of their economic and politi-cal system. I finally told him quite warmly to go away.

Several hours after I reached Erivan I took a chauffeur-driven car to Etchmiadzin where I met an old man who carried an obsolete musket. He said he was the guard of the ruins of the nearby church, called Zvartnotz Vank. We walked among the ruins and came to an apricot tree which the old man shook, whereupon half a dozen small apricots fell to the grass beneath the tree. We picked up the apricots and ate them, and he remarked that the apricots were small this year. Last year, he said, they were small, too, but not as small as they were this year. When we came to the open plains beyond the ruins I said suddenly, "Where is Bitlis?"

The old man looked at me, and I saw laughter come into his eyes.

"Your family is from Bitlis? Is that it?"

"Yes."

To the right was Ararat. The old man turned a little to the

left and looked far out on the golden grass of the rolling plains. He stiffened his right arm at his side, then lifted it slowly as if it were a mechanical device designed specifically for the purpose of indicating the way to Bitlis. Now, he leveled his vision along the length of his arm, as if his arm were a rifle.

"Bitlis," he said. "Straight ahead is Bitlis. If you walk six days and six nights you will reach Bitlis. Walk, then."

I burst into laughter, for he had performed for my amusement as well as for his own, and he himself chuckled softly.

One frequently hears of somebody or other that he is a character out of a book. I will not say such a thing of the old man, however. He was a man out of the earth and life of Armenia, an unschooled peasant whose whole life had been difficult. But the first thing he did was to shake the apricot tree in order to share with me, a stranger, the little that he had.

I stayed in Erivan six or seven days, and then it was time to continue my travels: to Tiflis, to Batum, by ship to Sevastopol on the Black Sea, and from there by train to Moscow.

A day or two after my arrival in Moscow I was taken by a young woman guide of the Intourist to pay my respects to the celebrated poet Yeghishe Charentz, who occupied a suite of rooms with a balcony at the best hotel in town. My own hotel, the New Moscow, was a little west of Red Square, past St. Basil's and the Moscow River. East of Red Square, in the heart of town, was the hotel where Charentz was living at that time. The guide took me up in the elevator to the third floor and together we walked down a corridor and stopped at an open door. From somewhere inside Charentz appeared quickly, smiling. We shook hands and greeted one another in Armenian. He then spoke in Russian to the young woman, and she went off, saying in English that she would leave us alone and return in an hour or so.

It was late afternoon of a day in June, in 1935, and ever since Charentz has been in my thoughts. I have wanted to write about him, but I have not done so for several reasons. First, because my writing might be misunderstood and thereby bring him embarrassment, anxiety, personal difficulty, or even misfortune. I could not have such a possibility on my conscience. I could only pray from year to year that, wherever he happened to be, his fate and fortune might not be too much for him. I felt deeply grateful that I had met him at all, and while he himself never urged me not to write about him, or about Soviet Armenia or Soviet Russia, I felt that it was personal courage and pride which prohibited him from doing so, and I sensed that his straightforward, warm, and gallant manner toward me was the consequence of an implicit trust in my discretion. Second, I did not write about him because he is a poet whose poetry I do not know, since he writes in Armenian which I do not read. And finally, because I saw him only three or four times.

A few things, however, I believe I may say about Charentz. To begin with, I am afraid I was unable not to be astonished that he was very small and very ugly. I am sure Charentz must have noticed my astonishment, but if he did, he did not permit me to notice. In surely less than half a minute he was no longer a small man. His size was entirely irrelevant. And instead of being an ugly man, he was handsome. His voice had warmth, and his eyes were direct, swift and intelligent. Charentz was not a small body with a large rather grotesque head and a huge hooked nose. He was a living personality, whose place of residence, the body, was by accident what it was. I found it impossible not to feel proud to be in his presence, and he in turn made me feel he was happy to have me in his presence. But I do not mean that our conversation was routine in its cordiality, or that all we did was compliment one another. Quite the contrary. Having met as countrymen and fellow-writers, such routine courtesy was soon put aside, and we spoke as if we had always been friends but simply had not met before.

I liked Charentz straight off, but more important than this was the feeling I had that he was a truly great man. Human greatness is a rather difficult thing to account for, and more often than not one is mistaken in one's hunches about somebody one has met. Charentz seemed great to me, I think, because he was made of a mixture of proud virtues and amusing flaws. On the one hand, his independence of spirit was balanced by a humorous worldliness, his acute intelligence by a curiosity that frequently made him seem naïve, his profoundly gentle manners by a kind of mocking mischievousness which might easily be mistaken for rudeness. But he was never rude, he was witty, and the purpose of his wit was to keep himself from the terrible condition of pomposity. He was swift, and there was a quality in him of both passion and violence —the violence of a creative man whose passion for truth has been tricked and troubled by unavoidable forces. These forces seemed to have compelled a wise but nevertheless uncomfortable moral expediency. Now, I had found a number of eminent Armenians whom I had met in Armenia and Russia quite guarded in their conversations with me. I might, for instance, ask what seemed to me a most innocent question about the life of Armenians in a certain town, and I might hear a reply full of caution, indefiniteness, evasion, and even suspicion. This was a new experience for me, but I was able soon enough to understand the necessity for such caution. Charentz, however, simply could not be bothered. He said precisely what he wanted to say at any given point of a conversation, and his speech was full of that order of contradiction which is the mark of the spirit which is still free and still eager not to forfeit its freedom. At the same time, however, he might suddenly say something preposterous and unacceptable. But whenever this happened I noticed that he chuckled or said something under his breath, as if to himself. I did not find his Armenian, or his speed of speech, difficult to follow, for he spoke with great simplicity. Nor did he find my Armenian at all confusing to him. As a matter of fact, I never found it necessary to repeat any remark, or to put it another way.

Charentz said, "You write in English, but you are an Armenian writer just the same." I remarked that while I did not know his writing, it seemed to me that although he wrote in Armenian, he was essentially a world writer. Charentz said, "Perhaps, or let us hope so, although it would be quite enough to be an Armenian writer." Now, there is no need to expect that I have remembered the precise words that Charentz and I exchanged so many years ago, for I haven't. The greater part of the meaning of what we said I have not forgotten, but the actual words I have.

Charentz informed me that he had repudiated his earliest writing, and I told him that it didn't matter that he had done so, because the writing had its own life and he himself could no more end that life than I could. Charentz looked at me and smiled quickly. "Yes, that is true, isn't it?"

Now, when he said that he had repudiated his earliest writing I got the feeling that he expected me to believe him, but when I remarked that I didn't believe him, I got the feeling that he was quite glad that I didn't. And that is an example of how our conversation moved along. The better part of the value of the conversation was not so much in what was actually said as in the true meaning of what was said, based upon the reason behind the remark, and upon that which was simultaneously communicated *without* the use of words, by a pause, a glance, an inflexion.

I found Charentz bursting with energy and ideas, with intensity and health, but a moment later I was not at all surprised to find that he was also quite profoundly troubled in spirit and ill in body. He asked suddenly to be excused a moment while he administered medical treatment to himself with a needle. There was no explanation or awkwardness on his part. I stepped out on the balcony and watched the people in the streets. After a moment, he came out on the balcony and we continued our conversation as if there had been no interruption. But after that I had to wonder about his life —his whole life, from childhood to boyhood to early manhood— and I knew it had been laden over from the beginning with pain, sorrow, frustration, anger, bitterness, hatred, and all of the other things which will kill one man and carry another to greatness. His laughter on the balcony was heartier than ever, but in it now I heard great and almost unbearable sorrow and anguish, too.

In Erivan I had met many young and old Armenians, and I had felt that they were all members of my family, including even those I disliked. But it was not until I had reached Moscow that I came upón an Armenian who seemed to me both the most challenging of all as a person, and by all odds the most evolved, civilized, worthwhile, intelligent, troubled, unhappy, and yet somehow right, as the symbol of the indestructible spirit of Armenian life and culture—anywhere in the world. I wished Charentz could come to America for a visit, or even to live. He smiled at the idea and shook his head almost imperceptibly. "I am here," he said. "You are there. Someone else is somewhere else. So let it be."

I thought of Charentz as a brother, and I still do. I have met many writers in many countries, but I have met none who impressed me more than Charentz, and I still do not know his writing, and very little about his life. This slight memoir of him is entirely without politics. I liked him. I admired him. I was proud to be a countryman of his, and a fellow-writer. I am devoted to his memory.

Joe Gould, Joe Frisco,
and American Talk

Joe Gould, Joe Frisco, and American Talk was written in November 1956 for *Time and Tide* magazine in London. Now and then every American writer gets a request to send a foreign magazine a letter—a kind of report. I have had such requests from Dublin, London, Paris, Stockholm, Belgrade, Bucharest, Prague, Moscow, Tokyo, Sydney, and several other cities. Most of the time I have answered the request instantly. Whenever it hasn't been instantly answered, it hasn't been answered at all—not because I didn't want to respect the request, but because it is always a matter of now or never. There is generally no payment, but this doesn't condition my thinking at all. The fact is I have always felt under personal obligation to answer all requests from foreign countries. And I have always regretted unwittingly not doing so. I am not a member of P.E.N., or of any other official literary group or order, but I do feel a personal responsibility to readers and writers all over the world. There is scarcely a country in which somebody has not read in his own language something I wrote in English, which somebody translated. I do permit myself to notice that nothing I have ever written has been destructive, hateful, anti-people, anti-life, or anti-God—anybody's God. And so, thinking of readers of my stuff in faraway places and among some of the smaller tribes of the human family, I feel that I am a friend, and I am pleased and proud whenever I read that I am taken for one.

What a people talk about means something. What they don't talk about means something.

American talk is not grim. If anything, it tends to be silly among the successful; witless among the eminent; dishonest among the ambitious; repetitious among the specialists; and just plain boring among the well-adjusted.

Only comics and characters, like Joe Frisco and Joe Gould, are likely to say something when they open their mouths. Joe Frisco stutters. Joe Gould mumbles through a ragged tobacco-stained beard. Both are legends.

Joe Frisco is a song and dance man, about seventy, whose act is one of the greatest of all time. He hasn't worked steadily in perhaps thirty years because he won't cut his wage, which is $2,000 a week. He goes to the races and bets the horses.

Joe Gould, also about seventy, is a writer, prose and poetry. *The Oral History of the World* has never been finished. According to Joe Gould, great amounts of it have been misplaced, lost, stolen, thrown away, or accidentally burned. Only one fragment of it, to my knowledge, has appeared in print, in *The Dial*, about thirty years ago. It was the most promising writing by an American I have ever read. His sonnet Quack consists of fourteen lines of that word. It is a sonnet for recitation only, and so far only Joe Gould himself has recited it straight through. He comes from the Gould family which is *known* as the Gould family, he went to Harvard, his store of information is encyclopaedic, he likes to drink beer, he has no money, nobody knows how he keeps alive—or in fact if he is alive in November, 1956.

On a visit to the Tax Collector's office in Hollywood Joe Frisco was informed that he owed a hundred and sixty-two thousand dollars in back taxes. He was asked what he had done with the money. "I spent it—on cigars," he stuttered. On his way out he saw an anxious young comedian sitting on the bench in the hall. The young comic said he was worried because he owed the Tax Collector three thousand dollars and wasn't working. "Forget it," Joe Frisco told him. He turned and called out to the man who had just interviewed him, "Put the kid's tab on my account, will you?"

The producer of Information Please once telephoned Joe Gould to invite him to appear on the popular radio program as a guest—for a good fee. Joe refused to talk to the man. "A thing like that would be an invasion of my privacy," he said. At that time he was sleeping in Central Park if he was uptown, and in the doorways of Greenwich Village if he was downtown.

Joe Frisco and Joe Gould, both homeless, owners of nothing, aged but young (or at any rate unadjusted), are among the last of the American eccentrics. Both are rare and talented men. The song and dance man enjoyed brilliant fame and fortune in his youth, and then let it go. The writer never enjoyed wide fame, never published a book, never made a dollar from writing, but busier writers with dozens of books published have long since faded out of memory. But whoever has met Joe Frisco or Joe Gould will not forget him.

It is possible to believe these two are entitled to be grim in their talk, but the fact is they aren't grim.

Eugene O'Neill was grim from the beginning, and the grimness came to greatness in The Iceman Cometh, in which O'Neill said man is a liar, a crook, a spiritual criminal, a puny whining miserable fraud, who must nevertheless be carefully noticed and tenderly loved. Broadway hated the play.

Americans still believe they are cut out to be successful—in everything: love, love-making, luck, luck-giving, money-making, sense-making, cancer-avoiding, clothes-wearing, car-driving, and so on.

In his plays O'Neill talked about Americans as if he had expected them to be a great race involved in the achievement of a great and meaningful order of grace. The other plays of his time were clever trivia, or tortured turns at realism, inevitably hysterical and unbearable. But Americans consider the unbearable in art a mark of greatness. This figures. Americans do not believe art is lived.

Americans want (and perhaps need) money and things. They want and need the national theory of importance and power. This makes for dull talk.

Americans don't know enough to be grim. They want things, and it keeps them busy.

The politicians know this, and both political parties itemize what they have given or will give and what the other party promised but didn't give. Nobody believes a word of it. It's talk and it's necessary and right, and if something good doesn't come of it, perhaps something bad won't, either. It never really matters who said what, and who didn't. Somebody said it.

Americans aren't sure who they are, or who they want to be. In the meantime, there's money and things. It runs through all of their talk, which is so dull nobody really listens to anybody else unless the speaker is somebody like Joe Frisco or Joe Gould.

Look Out,
Here Comes Another Lion

Look Out, Here Comes Another Lion was written in 1954 and sent to a big magazine in the hope that the piece would fetch a thousand dollars and permit me to feel like a millionaire for a day or two, but the editor of the magazine sent it back, saying nobody is interested in the trials and tribulations of writers, everybody wants to read stories about people. Now, of course, if any people *are* people, it's writers, and not super-people, either, just plain, ordinary people. Still, there is this discrimination against them, but I didn't feel like arguing with the editor. The fact is I never argue with an editor, and hardly ever with anybody else. If I find myself arguing, I know I'm sick. One *knows,* one doesn't argue, and that's the end of it. When an editor tells me why he doesn't want something I have sent him, all I understand is that he doesn't want it. And I must then either put the thing aside, or try it on another editor. I remember that in 1954 I had to have a few dollars in a hurry, so that when this piece came back I decided to send it to a magazine that might just let me have a few dollars quickly—not a thousand dollars, but perhaps a hundred. I sent it to *The Rotarian,* the official magazine of one of ten or eleven "service" clubs in the nation, whose members I have always been obliged to regard as either harmless bores or clever crooks—which I consider to be none of my business. They had a magazine, I had a piece of writing, I needed money, I sent them the piece, they bought it, paid me $100, and no harm done. The surprising thing is that the editor accepted the piece, but sometimes these things happen. Sherwood Anderson once wrote, "Nobody asked me to write. It was my own idea. My troubles are of no interest to anybody else." Or as one of the better songs of the past decade puts it, "You've got your troubles, I've got mine." All the same, it made me feel good that the time spent in writing the piece had not been entirely wasted. When I need money, earning it makes me feel good, perhaps because I have never had and don't expect to have any other source of income. I can neither get, nor do I desire to get, money from relatives, friends, foundations, endowments, national trusts, or by means of prizes or awards. I wouldn't know how to fill out the forms involved. When I can't pay my way with money earned by writing, I will have to earn money by doing some other kind of work.

One day an old acquaintance said, "I've quit writing. It's not for me."

Ordinarily I go along with Joe's little joke and tell him one of my own, but this time he *wasn't* joking.

"I haven't written anything in a year," he said. "I'm finished at 44, I don't want to be bothered any more. The critics I don't respect say I'm great. The critics I do respect say I'm bad. And the stuffy critics don't say anything at all."

"Do you mean," I said, "you're interested in what the critics say?"

"I *was*," Joe said. "I'm not any more, because I'm not interested in writing at all any more. I've quit. I never did find out why I ever got into writing in the first place, but I know exactly why I got out."

"Why?"

"First, because I can't make a living at it. Second, because my writing doesn't improve. Why don't you quit, too?"

"I don't know," I said, "but I do know why I started in the first place."

"Why?" Joe asked.

"Well," I said, "when I was in the first grade at Emerson School in Fresno, I was astonished to discover that three little boys knew how to read and write, and I didn't. Their parents had taught them at home. And then a year later when I was in the second grade I was astonished again. This time I discovered that everybody in the class knew how to read and write, and I still couldn't."

"Why not?"

"I don't know, but I just couldn't, that's all. Furthermore, I didn't *believe* in reading and writing. I considered them a trick for which there was no sensible reason. Even so, I worried a lot about my stupidity. Now, in my family at that time there was a man named Hovagim who was considered to be one of the kindest men out of Bitlis. I was sitting on the steps of my house one day after school when Hovagim came up and said, "You seem awfully troubled for a man only 38 years old."

"'Eight,' I said. "'I'll be eight next August.'"

"'I had no idea. Now, what's the trouble?'"

"'I can't read.'"

"'Is that so?'"

"'I can't write, either.'"

"The kind man eased himself down on the steps and sat beside me. I felt sure he would have a secret to tell me in a moment that would make it possible for me to learn to read and write tomorrow, and I wasn't mistaken."

"What did he tell you?" Joe said.

"'Can't read or write, is that it?'"

"'Yes, sir.'"

"'Want to read and write, is that correct?'"

"'Yes, sir.'"

"'Plan to be around for some time to come?'"

"'Yes, sir.'"

"'Nothing else of any kind the matter?'"

"'No, sir.'"

"'Eat good, run good, play good, sleep good?'"

"'Yes, sir. How can I learn to read and write?'"

"What did he say to *that*?" Joe said.

"He told me to try my best *not* to learn to read and write."

"Did *that* make sense to you?"

"It did."

"What happened?"

"Well, all I know is that in less than a month I had not been able not to learn to read and write, and what's more, I had been unable not to suspect the whole beauty of the alphabet itself, and the whole meaning and purpose of language itself."

"Is that supposed to tell me why you became a writer in the first place?" Joe said.

"Yes, it is. I became a writer because during several of the most important years of my life writing seemed to me to be the most unreal, unattractive, and unnecessary idea ever imposed upon the human race."

"O.K.," Joe said. "You're trying to tell me something. What is it?"

"When you *really* quit writing, you won't know it."

About a year later Joe's ninth novel came out. A great many critics said it was great. I read it, and it was no good at all—nervous, sick, dirty, and essentially pathetic. One day Joe sent this telegram: "Now, I'm sure I don't know how to write, but I can use the money, so I guess I'll pretend I believe the critics, God help me."

We met at a party in his honor a month later and I said, "That was a funny telegram you sent, but the fact is your ninth novel *is* bad. What's the matter with you?"

He turned and walked away, an outraged literary lion, and I haven't seen him since.

The Turk Street Gamblers

The Turk Street Gamblers was written in 1954 and sold to one of the earlier *Playboy*-style magazines, *Escapade,* which was published somewhere in Hollywood. One of its editors, Don Anderson, had written to invite me to send *Escapade* a story, for which I would be paid $500. I am always happy to have an editor ask me for something, no matter what his magazine is. I remember with happiness receiving a letter in Malibu from a baking company in Milwaukee which invited me to pass along a few words of philosophy to publish in their company magazine. Quite a few American writers had obliged them, although there was no payment. I couldn't resist the invitation to philosophize quickly in my reply, and then to suggest that perhaps the company might be willing to send me some samples of what *they* manufacture and sell. After waiting two weeks I presumed the company hadn't liked my philosophizing, hadn't wanted to go to the trouble of packing and shipping samples, or like so many people who want stuff for nothing, forget the sender the minute they get the stuff. But one fine day a Parcel Post truck stopped at 24848 Malibu Road, and a man brought down a large box, containing one package of every kind of cracker and cookie manufactured by the company. This was indeed a delight to me—once again a little something or other in the great world of transaction had been achieved. The crackers and cookies were good, too. I had one or two of each every day for about three months.

The Turk Street Gamblers is part of my story. I needed to gamble, that's the long and short of it. I liked gambling, I felt great when I won, and for many years I won at everything—rummy, poker, horse races, dice, prize fights. I had good luck because I insisted on it.

Good luck was central to my attitude about myself, the world, and others—I didn't want to take money away from anybody who needed money, I wanted to take it away from the establishment, the specialists, the rich, the con men, the criminals, the cheaters, and the economic system itself. As my luck at gambling continued, suddenly my luck at writing broke through, too. I hurdled the limitations of both the editors of magazines and the editors of book publishers, and I was suddenly not only published, but famous—as myself, a named new writer with his own unmistakable style.

Until I was 30, gambling and writing were closely related in my heart and mind, and in the lore and religion by which I was making my way to some kind of personal meaning, effectiveness, and responsibility to others.

In the end, though, the gambling got entangled in war, marriage, army, kids, love, loneliness, despair, helplessness, anger, hatred, madness, sickness, confusion, doubt, indecision, and so, of course, gambling lost its innocence. It suddenly became enormous, desperate, stupid, and destructive. The kind of world in which crooks become millionaires while kids get killed at war games made me want to get rich without working. (For the likes of me, however, that is just not permitted.)

I often think of the writers I used to see gambling on Turk Street. Where are they? Where are they now, poor bastards? As for the professional gamblers, I think of them, too. Most of them are long since dead; they were in fact dead in the poker games, waiting for the nuts, as it was put—day after day, week after week.

Turk Street in San Francisco in 1935 was a favorite playground for a wide variety of indoorsmen—card-sharps, bookies, horseplayers, stud and lowball amateurs and professionals, crapshooters, barflies, and common loafers.

Among the poker amateurs were a number of fiction writers, including myself. Another was a Finn who had had two novels published, and quite a few action stories in the pulps. A third was a fellow with a bulging brow who had had one novel published, and a dozen or more stories in magazines like *The Saturday Evening Post* and *Cosmopolitan*. On the side he reviewed books for an old-time San Francisco weekly called *The Argonaut*, but he never read the books he reviewed.

"As I understand it," he said, "Ambrose Bierce, Mark Twain, and Bret Harte themselves once wrote for *The Argonaut*, and I thought I'd better, too, since I'm not a native son, either."

"I believe they wrote for *The Overland Monthly*," the Finn re-marked. To which the man with the bulging brow replied, "Well, anyhow, they came out to San Francisco from the East and the Midwest, and so did I. The native sons don't know the first thing about writing, because they don't understand cycles. Instead of staying here, they're supposed to go to New York and Boston."

Besides published writers Turk Street had all manner of un-published ones, especially after word got around that a lot of talk around the poker table in the back room at Joe Bailey's was literary. The place became a kind of writing school, and sitting in on a game became something like taking an extension course in the art of fiction and poetry. Published poets, however, were infrequent visitors, but they *did* show up now and then—only to watch. A fiction writer with five bucks was always eager to take a seat at the poker table, but a writer of poetry with ten dollars in his pocket wouldn't think of risking the money. The caution of poets is some-thing worth looking into, most likely.

Over Joe Bailey's, Oscar Gill ran a crap game. On occasion he put two or three blackjack tables and dealers to work, too. And he booked horse race bets. I called him Eric after Eric Gill of England —a devout man whose sculpture I had seen in photographic reproductions in books at the Public Library: a man who designed type, studied religion, and wrote a very special order of prose (since he was a very special order of man). Oscar Gill was another order entirely, although in his own way he was special enough, too.

The tradition of bookies is to lose with grace and to pay off with a smile, as if the bookie were delighted to have a winner among his clients, but Oscar Gill had no use for that tradition. He believed there must be a mistake, and then when there wasn't, he disputed the amount bet, and after the dispute had been settled, he insisted that the client bet back the total amount involved on the next race. If the client preferred not to, which he generally did, Oscar sulked and went into hiding in the small room just beyond the betting counter. Sometimes he would be gone for five minutes, sometimes until post-time for the next race. He would look at the winning-client out of the eyes of a deeply wounded and terribly persecuted humanitarian, and then he would bring out a thin wad of currency and count out the sum involved—but it was always five or ten dollars short. A number of winners just didn't have the heart to point this out to Oscar. They took what he had counted out, and let it go at that. Now and then, though, a writer would point out the error, and a fresh wound would be inflicted on Oscar's soul. He would pick up the currency quickly and go back into his hideout. In the end, though, he would pay off, but first he would say, "Good thing you writers have got old Oscar Gill to pay your food and rent bills. But what do *you* guys ever do for Oscar?"

Nothing, of course—just bet with him, and most of the time lose.

Joe Bailey walked like a duck, thought things out calmly, and made a decision. Oscar Gill, on the other hand, bounced, as if there were little Pogo sticks under each of his feet. He faced all problems swiftly and a little hysterically, and *never* reached a decision. Joe and Oscar weren't partners in any real sense, although being neighbors they were mutually interested in their clients, since their income was derived from them, and they hired the same help.

Joe Bailey's best stud-dealer was a young Italian from somewhere in the North Beach who was called Spider, most likely because his hands were all over the table to see that nobody got away with any kind of cheating. For a little extra money Spider now and then dealt blackjack for Oscar Gill, too.

Spider was an indoor man. He loved to be inside places, preferably disreputable ones. He was slim and pale and swift, and by any standards excepting those of the insurance companies, healthy. After work he loved to duck across the street to the Bay City Grill with one of the girls of the street and have a thick New York cut steak while she paid for her own plate of hash, or ham and eggs. This meal might be at two in the morning, or three or four. From the Bay City he would cross Turk Street quickly—he hated to be outdoors—and duck back into Joe Bailey's. With whatever money was left from his day's wages he would take a seat in the pan game. If he won, and he was pretty lucky, he would send one of Joe Bailey's floor boys to the Greek grocer's at the corner of Turk and Taylor, and the Greek would pass along to the boy a bottle of Johnny Walker Black Label—the only kind of Scotch Spider would drink, since he had heard it was the best, and the best was none too good for him. Spider would tip the boy a buck, open the bottle, take a swig, and settle down to a lot of a happy pan.

Joe Bailey's never closed. In 1935 when I went to Europe for the first time my starting point was the stud table in the back room. Spider was dealing, the Finn novelist had the seat to his left, Hollywood Pete the following one, I was next, and after me came a huge old gentleman called Big Gus, then a man we called Mahkhamovitz because he said Mahkhamovitz every time he lost—when pronounced properly it means the Angel of Death in Yiddish—and finally Curley, a smiling fat little man of sixty or so who played better stud than anybody I ever saw. When it was time for me to go I got up and said so long. Spider reached across the table, and we shook hands.

"You take care of yourself now," he said. "Watch out for them card sharps on the boats."

I was away from San Francisco about six months. The day I got home I went back to Joe Bailey's, and there at the stud table was Spider and all the others who had been there when I said good-bye, except Big Gus, who had died. I sat down and took an ace from Spider for my hole card, and then another ace. I was very lucky that night, and I did a lot of brandy-drinking. It was almost as if I had never left the game, although I was sorry about Big Gus.

Every now and then the town got hot, and Joe Bailey and Oscar Gill waited nervously for the police to shut them down—generally it was only for a day or two; or at the most a week or two, and then all would be well again. The writers would come back and sit down and talk about writing, or anything else that came to mind.

One time, though, both joints were shut down for a month, and then for another month, so that Spider was out of work, and therefore in trouble. Spider needed to deal. He needed to be indoors in a pleasant atmosphere. He needed his pay. He needed his steaks at the Bay City, and his chats with the girls of the street, but now he was out of work, and the back room at Joe Bailey's was deserted. Spider's clothes were wearing out. He was out of funds. A number of writers kept a straight shot of Black Label in front of him at the bar adjoining Joe Bailey's—it was Joe's bar of course—but that just wasn't Spider's style. He didn't like to have others buy him drinks. He looked all right, but he was lost. The writers, for want of a better place to loaf, met at the bar almost every night and talked and made bets on various things—all kinds of things, almost anything, for writers get bored a little quicker than office-workers. They'd bet a dollar or two about the next girl off the street who would step into Joe's saloon for a shot—blonde or brunette, redhead or black. They'd bet on what the next loafer from the street would have to drink: Scotch, rye, or beer. They'd bet on how soon Sam the bartender would say to somebody, "What's it all about, boy?" And so they wouldn't be so bored, a little money would change hands, and another night would slip away.

One evening the Finn said to another writer, "Where's Spider these days?"

The other writer said, "I haven't seen him in about a month. Have you?"

"No," the Finn said, and then he challenged the other writer to make a bet involving a fly on Sam's nose, but while they were settling the terms of the bet, Sam brushed the fly away, so they were forced to devise another bet, which they soon managed.

They bet a hundred dollars Spider would never work at Joe Bailey's again, because the work wasn't steady and Spider couldn't stand being humiliated by poverty. That is, the Finn took *that* side, and the other writer took the other—that is, that Spider *would* be back at Joe Bailey's when it opened again.

A whole year went by, and there I was with a Packard convertible I had bought for a hundred dollars, and now I was almost broke. I had met a Standard Oil credit man at Joe's bar, and he had brought me a credit card, and I had run up a bill of three hundred dollars, although I had only driven around town. The car used a lot of gas, but it looked like a car a famous new writer *ought* to drive. It had a condition called vapor-lock, too. The motor would get overheated in five minutes, and then if the car was brought to a stop at a stop sign it wouldn't start any more. The result was that I got quite a few tickets for jumping stop signs. I had been writing stories and sending them to editors, but I hadn't sold any of them for money enough to pay my gas bill, and I was running out of saloon money, too. A couple of Hollywood agents had sent me telegrams from time to time saying they had easy work for me with good pay at one or another of the movie factories. How about it? I hadn't answered their wires, but now it looked as if I'd have to, so I did, and the next evening I went to Hollywood by United Air Lines.

The following morning at nine I was at B. P. Schulberg's, across from Paramount, and I was on salary for the first time in years—$300 a week. It was embarrassing, but it just couldn't be avoided, that's all. The first day I put in a good day's work because I have always believed an honest hired hand *should*—I wrote the scenario for a whole feature musical. It was called Daily News, and I presented it to Ben myself. He glanced at the thirty pages, and then he said, "What do you say we go have a drink?"

It was after seven anyhow, and very nearly everybody else had gone home long ago. We went to Lucie's just up Melrose and had three at the bar, and then steaks. From Lucie's we drove out Sunset, and then up a hill to a big parking lot adjoining a building that looked something like a government building at Versailles. The place was called the Clover Club and you had to be somebody to get in. Ben was somebody, and he got me in.

Well, it was a great place. Roulette tables, crap tables, black-jack tables—all surrounded by studio owners, producers, directors, male and female stars, scenario writers, and a few riffraff—commonplace millionaires.

Ben went his way while I studied the joint—to see if I could find an appropriate spot where I might put my eleven dollars to work without appearing to be a cheapskate, or an out-of-towner. I found a number of alcohol-drenched writers wearily betting blackjack only one chip at a time, but the chips turned out to be worth a hundred dollars apiece.

I kept wandering around among the celebrities, and then at last I found a blackjack table at which were seated three little old ladies. They were the mothers of producers, I was later informed, and they were betting silver dollars. I sat among them, put out a dollar, took my cards, and they were the worst: 16. The dealer waited for me to let him know whether to hit.

I looked up, and there was Spider, only now he looked like a Decathlon Champion of the Olympic Games. His face was full and tanned. His eyes were rested and calm. And his suit must have cost a hundred and fifty—made to order. I was about to give him the old Frisco greeting when he just barely smiled, and then just barely shook his head.

"Card?" he said.

I said yes, and he gave me a picture.

While he was picking up the cards he looked at me again, and again he just barely smiled, so the next time around I bet *two* dollars. I got a jack and a king to his ten and eight. I let it ride. Going along slow and easy, in less than half an hour I had more than two hundred dollars, and the little mothers had barely held their own, if in fact they had done that.

I looked at Spider, and then at the stacked silver dollars in front of me, and again he just barely smiled. This time he leaned his head a little to the left. After a moment I looked to the left and got the idea: the bar.

I converted the silver to chips, and the chips to currency, and then went to the bar and asked the bartender for two double shots of Black Label. He poured them, and went off. I waited for Spider, and after three or four minutes he came over and burst into laughter.

"I never thought I'd ever see you here," he said. "Have you given up book-writing?"

"Just for a little while. I'm down here to get out of debt, that's all."

He sipped the whiskey instead of gulping it down the way he used to do in San Francisco.

"Got to stay sober," he explained.

"We kept looking for you at Joe's bar," I said.

"San Francisco's shot," Spider said. "I couldn't take it. Where you working?"

"I'm over at Ben Schulberg's. I just got in today."

"How much you owe?"

"About fifteen hundred, counting everything, but I figure as long as I'm here anyhow I might as well hang around until I can go back with three or four thousand in my pocket."

"That's not easy to do in this town," Spider said. "You make it, but you spend it, too. There's guys out there at the wheel or the table who make three, four, five thousand a week. *They* can't quit working, either."

I was pretty sure Spider had given me winning cards at the blackjack table, but I couldn't come out and say so. Instead I said, "I sure had a run of luck at blackjack, didn't I?"

"Yes, you did," Spider said, "but then you know how luck is. Who's around up home?"

"The same old gang," I said, "but they're lost without the action. They meet at the bar and try to invent bets to make. I made a few myself. I bet the Finn a hundred dollars we'd see you back dealing at Joe Bailey's. How about it?"

"You lose, kid," Spider said. "I can't go back. I can't afford it. Hell, this ain't the only suit I've got like this. I've got three more. And shoes? I'm having them made in England, the same as the stars. And I've only been here two months. This place is like home to me now. The money's big and fast. And don't think Spider doesn't get his share."

Spider finished his drink, looked at his watch that must have cost two or three hundred, and then he said, "Kid, it's like old times just seeing a face from Frisco. I got to go back now."

"When I get back to San Francisco I'll pay the Finn."

"You never know. *This* place may get raided, too, but if it does and I come home, I'll be loaded."

"Before you go, Spider, tell me one thing. Where'd you get that tan? I never saw you looking so healthy before."

A pained expression came over Spider's face.

"Man," he said, "you don't know what happened to me when I left Frisco. You know I was flat. I'd hocked or sold everything I had. I was out-of-doors two whole months, man. I'll never go out-of-doors again. It's murder. I can't take sunshine. It makes me stupid. Do you know for two weeks I even worked on a vineyard in Fresno? Never again. Well, take care of yourself. Get home and get back to your book-writing. Any fast-talking phony can write movie stories. I see 'em in here all the time."

He went off quickly, and a few minutes later I saw him begin to deal to the little mothers. He was home again, indoors, where he belonged.

Three months later my bills were paid. I had written a lot of movie stuff for Ben Schulberg, and then for Harry Cohn at Columbia, but nobody wanted any of the stuff. I guess it was because I had written it without making a lot of fuss. I didn't have three or four thousand dollars in my pocket, I had sixty dollars, but I decided to go home and back to book-writing just the same.

When I went down to Joe Bailey's on Turk Street in San Francisco I saw two unpublished writers out front talking, so I knew the place was open again. I didn't have a hundred dollars for the Finn, but I could at least let him know I had lost. I could pay him some now, and the rest later on, but he wasn't at the stud table, or upstairs at Oscar Gill's, or in the bar.

I asked Joe Bailey about him, and Joe thought about the matter a moment, and then he made his decision.

"I think he's dead, kid. He hasn't been around in months."

Well, I never did see the Finn again, and I never saw another story of his in the pulps, or another book by him, either. If he hadn't died, he had certainly gone away, and he had certainly stopped writing.

I went upstairs to Oscar Gill's. As luck would have it Oscar himself was at the peephole. He sprung the door open and bowed reverently.

"The New York Kid himself," he said. "Where the hell have you been? We've got to have more writers around here. *Gambling* writers, not the kind that stand out front and talk. Get over there and take the dice."

"Old Eric Gill," I said.

"*Oscar,* not Eric," he said. "You never could get my name right, could you?"

"Oscar or Eric," I said. "What's the difference, just so your health's good?"

Old Oscar bounced on his little Pogo sticks, laughed and hollered to the stick boys, "Hey, boys, it's going to be like old times around here again."

It wasn't, though, but then of course it never is.

The Adventures of
American Writers
in Paris in 1929

The Adventures of American Writers in Paris in 1929 appeared in *The New Republic* in 1962. It is a book review, a form of writing I am not addicted to, perhaps because I take the job seriously, insist on carefully reading every word in the book I'm reviewing, and part of it two or three times. And I will not write a review unless I like a book.

One cannot abide certain writers whose writing one knows is good —one just can't like their writing for a variety of reasons: perhaps because the writer is a liar, a bully, a crook, a hater, a belittler of life, a half-wit, or something else. And yet his writing is skilled, professional, and irresistible. (But to me unreadable.) Books by such writers I refuse to review, but it doesn't matter, because I am almost never invited to do so. All such writers have great numbers of champions among the critics, and these champions review their books. All the same, one of the first things of mine I saw in print in a good magazine was a review of a book—in a book-reviewing contest. I got second prize. (Doesn't everybody?) *Scribner's*, 1929?

One of the first men mentioned in this review of Morley Callaghan's book, *That Summer in Paris*, is Edward J. O'Brien, and before I forget (again) I want to remember a walk I took with him in London in the month of July of the year 1939. I had made a point of getting to Europe once more before the beginning of the war that everybody knew was now unavoidable. My route was London, Paris, London, Dublin, and back to New York.

Edward J. O'Brien was the founder and editor of the yearly book entitled *The Best Short Stories*. American. British (including Irish). And now and then European. Everybody who was interested in the short story, whether to write or to read, was indebted to O'Brien, and I was especially so, and very grateful to him. We had been in touch by correspondence, but we now met for the first time, and went for an evening walk, during which we talked about the short story, writers, poets, readers, editors, history, Russia, Communism, Capitalism, Germany, Italy, Fascism, Spain, Franco, Hitler, Mussolini, Stalin. In short, we talked about everything everybody was talking about in those days. The term Communism continues to be used, but the term Capitalism has been dropped, and in its place the term Democracy is used. It was very difficult in those days, however, for a writer not to be sympathetic to what was known as the Communist or People's Cause, and to be angry about the Capitalist or Rich Man's Cause. The best novelists, story writers, and poets stood with the Communists or humanitarians, including a new group of writers clustered around W. H. Auden: Christopher Isherwood, Stephen Spender, Louis MacNiece, and C. Day Lewis, among others.

"But," O'Brien said, "I know these chaps, and they don't *like* people. As a matter of fact they can't stand them. I once saw three of them walking up Piccadilly when a beggar asked them for a coin. They pretended that he wasn't there, a man not much unlike themselves, as a matter of fact, but unfortunately not a writer and not a humanitarian."

Well, of course, there is a great deal of that sort of thing, and it's not really anybody's business. The writing itself of a writer is all anybody is concerned about.

In a list of books Yvor Winters sent me from Palo Alto in 1932 one was called *Last Spring They Came Over,* by a writer named Morley Callaghan. From San Francisco I had sent Mr. Winters some writing for a magazine called *Kaleidoscope* which Edward J. O'Brien had mentioned in his yearbook of the American short story. Mr. Winters had replied that the magazine was only a mimeographed one, with very few readers, and in any case it had been discontinued. He suggested I might read the books on the list he had prepared for his students at Stanford. I had heard of most of the books on the list and had read around in perhaps three or four of them, but then I was keen about writing, not reading. At the Public Library, to which I walked at least once a day during the Depression, I looked up every book on the list and gave it my undivided attention for anywhere from five minutes to fifty-five, which was about my limit. When I came to Morley Callaghan's book I was glad it was a collection of short stories because I liked that form best. I considered it the most natural of all literary forms, the most American, the most useful, and of course at that time the short story was the only thing I could write. I read the title story, Last Spring They Came Over, and said to myself, "This guy's pretty good. I'll read another." In no time I had read four of the stories, whereupon I quit, because now I *knew* Morley Callaghan *was* a writer, and that's all I really needed to know.

A few years later, in October of 1934, my own first book was published, also short stories: I was twenty-six, Morley Callaghan was thirty-one, Ernest Hemingway was thirty-six, and Scott Fitzgerald thirty-seven or thirty-eight.

Now, I'm dragging myself all over the place in this review of Callaghan's book for a reason. *That Summer in Paris, Memories of Tangled Friendships with Hemingway, Fitzgerald, and Some Others*, is a writer's book, about writers when they were young, when they were starting out. The summer involved was the summer of 1929. Some of the other writers were an almost-forgotten one who nevertheless had some very real importance at the time and in the book, Robert McAlmon, and a never-to-be forgotten one who figures only incidentally in the book, James Joyce.

That *was* a world, a very wonderful, funny, phony, stupid, romantic, laughing, posey, pathetic, sick and silly world. People wanted to be heroes. They wanted to be attractive and strong and superior and true and ruthless and honorable. Athletics was the thing, especially boxing. A man was stupid if he didn't know all about the most famous prizefighters and their little secrets of success. Well, actually, it wasn't people who wanted to be heroes, it was Ernest Hemingway, and Scott Fitzgerald.

Morley Callaghan's book is a tribute to that world and time, and to the two friends he did not see or hear from again after 1930 or thereabouts.

If the three of them were in Paris today (and in a sense they are), each would be a different kind of writer, mainly because of a different order of reality in the present world. Living was still personal in the late twenties: you didn't need any help from public events to make a fool of yourself. Hemingway appears to have been uneasy about the profession of writing insofar as it was the major preoccupation and activity of a strong man: its risks and dangers and difficulties just didn't seem enough in comparison with those of other loners: the prizefighter, the bullfighter, the criminal, the fighter-drunk. And so he took up boxing; only in Paris there was nobody to box, and then suddenly there was—Morley Callaghan.

This brings us to the central episode of the book: the match between Ernest Hemingway and Morley Callaghan, with Scott Fitzgerald serving as timekeeper: three extraordinary American writers, early in their careers, their best writing in the works or coming up in the next three or four years.

Fitzgerald and his Zelda are living it up in Paris.

Callaghan, just married, is in Paris with his Loretto because five years earlier he had met Hemingway on *The Toronto Star* and Hemingway had read his first stories and had encouraged him.

Also, Callaghan had sent stories from Toronto to Paris and Hemingway had handed them around to editor friends and acquaintances: Robert McAlmon, Hemingway's first publisher, for one: and Ford Madox Ford for another.

Now, of course there were many other writers in touch with the various editors and writers who were making a new literature at that time, but they have fallen by the wayside, so to put it. There are *always* many writers making a new literature. At the time it isn't easy to tell one from another.

Hemingway wanted to be told from the others.

His writing did it, but he didn't want only his writing to do it.

Faulkner didn't want to be known as a literary man: he claimed he was only a farmer. (I understand he actually wasn't, although he owned and lived on a farm.)

Morley Callaghan's book about Paris in 1929 is also about American writers running away from themselves, from their country, from their true natures, from the profession of writing.

And so one afternoon Hemingway, six feet something, perhaps 190 pounds, and Callaghan, five eight, and perhaps 170, picked up Fitzgerald, and went to the American Club for a routine contest of boxing. Hemingway and Callaghan had already had perhaps half a dozen such contests—friendly, unimportant, fun. But this time the timekeeper, Fitzgerald, was perhaps the handsomest, brightest, most successful, most truly wonderful new American writer in years, and so another writer, Hemingway, equally lucky, wanted to be especially impressive. The third writer, Callaghan, was liked by the other two for himself but also for the short stories he was writing and publishing, which became eventually the stories in the book Yvor Winters put on the list he sent to me.

Callaghan doesn't say, but one presumes the boxing contests with Hemingway were not prolonged—perhaps four regulation rounds of three minutes of boxing and one minute of rest.

Round one and Hemingway wants to look good, which means that Callaghan can get hurt if he isn't careful.

Round two. Hemingway wades in, Callaghan beats him to the punch, Hemingway is down. As Callaghan says in another context, it was as if the Woolworth Building had toppled. Consternation.

Embarrassment.

Fitzgerald puts it somewhat this way: "Oh my God, I let the round go *four* minutes."

Hemingway glares and rests.

Round three. Callaghan doesn't knock Hemingway down again, but neither does Hemingway knock Callaghan down, and Fitzgerald is watching and keeping time.

Round four and Callaghan is doing just fine. Hemingway is also doing just fine, which of course isn't enough.

Fitzgerald is mortified about something—about having let round two go an extra minute and thereby enabling or perhaps even compelling Callaghan to knock Hemingway down, or about Hemingway not living up to the picture Fitzgerald wanted to have of him as a prizefighter. (Thomas Wolfe, for instance, although a giant, was described to me as having been one of those overgrown lads who are puffy inside their skins, and quite soft, which wasn't the way I imagined he would be.)

Well, now, how were the three of them to get out of this unhappy predicament with egos intact, friendships intact, writing abilities intact, and all the rest of it?

The Champ just isn't fighting like a Champ, but if he tries *too hard*, Callaghan may just drop him again, and one gathers that Callaghan has no intention of throwing the fight.

At last somewhere in the fourth round (I'm inventing numbers and rounds, of course—the whole thing may have happened in *two* rounds) Callaghan, unhurt, unhit, accidentally slips to a knee or to both knees, and quickly Fitzgerald calls out something like this: "One knockdown for Callaghan, one for Hemingway."

And that's it, that's the story, that's the fight as it was fought. But it was a small part of another fight entirely. Each of the three writers was waging a fight of some kind that the others did not know about, could scarcely guess about, and could not help with.

Callaghan's fight seems to have been the easiest—simply to write well and to go on writing well, which he managed to do, which he is still doing, which he does in this book, slight and anecdotal as it is.

Scott and Zelda needed the human experience to be champagne all the time, and that of course is madness.

Hemingway was a very sensitive man who nevertheless was unable to take it easy about needing to be papa or the law or the best or the most, and so on.

Not long after my first book appeared a man got out of a taxi at 348 Carl Street in San Francisco and pressed the doorbell: Robert McAlmon, five or six years after the memorable summer Callaghan writes about. He is a fellow of medium height, a little worn-looking, probably a little rattled, confused, eager to talk, and with a grudge only against Hemingway, but why tell me about it? I hadn't been there. I knew nothing about Paris except what I had read in the little magazines. We went to Izzy's on Pacific Street, Izzy Gomes with his hat always on his head: grappa fizzes, beer, jokes, songs, laughter and that was the last I saw of McAlmon. I bought his book *Being Geniuses Together* and read it, and the fact is he *had* been there, he *had* helped Hemingway at the beginning, and he *could* write, but he *didn't*. Which raises the question, Who are the real writers?

They are the ones who write. And all the clinical reasons for their doing so, for their *needing* to do so, all of the belittling or enlarging reasons, mean absolutely nothing to that simple fact. The real writers are the writers who write, period.

In Paris in 1939 I stumbled upon a bookstore named Shakespeare & Company and I didn't even know it was a famous place. Somebody there, perhaps the lady who ran the place, put me on the telephone to speak to James Joyce, but I never met him. Morley Callaghan I met in New York in 1941. Edmund Wilson I met in Moscow in 1935. In San Francisco in 1936 I met Gertrude Stein and Alice B. Toklas. In London in 1944 and in Paris in 1945 I met Ernest Hemingway. Although I was in Hollywood once or twice when Scott Fitzgerald was there, I never met him. I saw Sherwood Anderson lecturing to women in Los Angeles, but I never spoke to him. I once met T. S. Eliot, but not Ezra Pound.

All of these people figure in Callaghan's book, and I feel a part of them, but I *know* I am *not* a part of them.

That Paris deal was quite a deal. There was something especially American about it. My San Francisco deal was rather Armenian, or at least European.

When I finally went to live in Paris, in 1959, I was fifty, and the idea was to learn how to make money enough by writing to be able to pay back taxes. I didn't learn, but then I wasn't very comfortable about the idea of learning something clever like that which involved something as stupid as money and how to get it and not need to hand it over to the mother government. But that's another story, although it's set in the same place: Paris.

Times change, the world changes, and that *had* been a time, and a world. And those *were* writers, and one of them, Morley Callaghan, writing easily, has kept the whole thing real in all of its youth and sorrow.

The Flashing Dragonfly

The Flashing Dragonfly appeared in *Nugget* in October 1962. *Nugget* was one of several girly magazines that was publishing writing as a sideline, long before *Playboy* hit the jackpot. When I was living like a famous rich young writer at the Hampshire House in New York, in 1939, Seymour Krim, 17 years old, working for *The New Yorker*, phoned one day, and I asked him up, so we could talk. I decided he was a good writer, and of course he was, and he is. About twenty-five years later, there he was all of a sudden on 5th Avenue, an editor at *Nugget*, for a living: Would I write him a piece, for $300? I went up to the Royalton Hotel at 44 West 44th Street, to room 1015, and during the next hour wrote the piece, mailed it to Seymour at the *Nugget*, which was not more than three hundred yards from the Royalton. And then I went to the Automat for a cup of coffee and a doughnut, a ritual started in New York in 1928 and maintained ever since. This is what I wrote.

Identity and attitude are of course inseparable, which is a stupid way of saying style is the man, which is a boring way of saying you're who you think you are, other people are not who they think they are, they are who you think they are. When a man is young he is probably sick if he doesn't think everybody else is a square and a phony, especially those who are past the age of 27, which is the last year of youth and truth. After 27, the human experience is only a prolonged burial ceremony with all kinds of pathetic diversionary acts, so that stiffs in their middle

30s may console themselves by becoming millionaires, or by holding public office, such as the Presidency, as it might be called, or by becoming the most unsuccessful abstract painter of the day and nation. Youth is the proper time to find the world and the human race false and hopeless, a theory that is neither arrogant nor inaccurate. Its only flaw is that it's useless.

What everybody wants to know is how does this inevitable falsity and hopelessness concern me, perhaps the first perfect specimen ever to reach the sidewalk of the world? How may I, neither false nor hopeless, pass along to everybody else what I am and have and know, so that they also, poor bastards, may be magnificent?

The attitude is rude, which in itself constitutes *size* at least, but rudeness soon slides into civility and then little by little into downright courtesy, or murder, and the kid's feeling of superiority is discovered to be a delusion, whereupon the world has a new adult. Whoever the kid had been, whoever had had the grand attitude, has finally heeded the admonishment of parents, teachers, governments, religions, and the law: "You just change your attitude now please, young man."

This transformation in kids—from flashing dragonflies, so to say, to sticky water-surface worms slowly slipping downstream—is noticed with pride by society and with mortification by God, which is a fantastic way of saying I don't like to see kids throw away their truth just because it isn't worth a dime in the open market.

Now, twice 27, it isn't likely that I shall ever be approached by representatives of the youth of Russia, China, Japan, Africa, Mississippi, Cincinnati, and Sacramento, for answers to the basic questions. The *exceptional* youth, I might have said; the regular or routine youth, being in charge of the world and everything else, would expect *me* to go to *them* for answers. Even so, perhaps I might be permitted to decide which *are* the basic questions, and then to answer them.

Perhaps the most basic of the questions is, "What is a fellow supposed to do in order to be so impressive that the most beautiful and desirable girls of Jersey City take for granted that he is the only man in the world?"

The answer to that question is this: Unless the man has majored in dentistry, in which case he must bring a lot of zip and dash to the filling of teeth cavities, the thing to do is to make an art of something that has never before been an art.

This can be done with almost any *thing*, and by the keeping and strengthening of the wild attitude, which can transform junk of all kinds, for instance, into sculpture for thoughtful exhibition at the Museum of Modern Art. Stuff found in the street, and *only* that stuff, could make a new reputation, and a fortune.

For the new painter the solution to the problem might be the size of the area to paint, or the shape: a circular fresco, for instance, might be most effectively achieved by having the painter (or artist) apply this paint from a moving motorcycle, or horse, or swing, or roller skates, or from stilts, but again the important thing is the attitude: the man must be big. But of course big is always big by comparison. As there is never any competition, it is very easy to be big.

That's sculpture and painting, accepted and traditional forms of art.

What about unknown forms?

Well, they are certainly *there*, and they can easily be revealed.

As a poor illustration of this, a new art might very well be the making of statements, such as this one: "I have just completed my first work of art, New York City, which I believe deserves to be carefully noticed."

Or this: "I have finally added 30 billion years to human time, so that it is now reasonable to believe immortality of some sort is not inconceivable. It was hard work."

Or: "Whenever you see an eye in any human being or animal, I hope you will have the decency to bear in mind that I invented eyes. I need the honor."

Another good bet is pomposity, but of course deadpan or dishonest pomposity, inasmuch as honest pomposity is only laughable. It is enjoyed by what is known in the vernacular as great men, and of course every country in the world has them. Dishonest pomposity on the other hand is something only an anarchist-genius can have. But the anarchist-genius is almost always anonymous, which makes this branch of superior inferiority appealing only to a few kids in the whole world at any given time.

Crime in any of its pathetic forms is useless. Literal stealing, for instance, is ridiculous, while stealing which appears to be philanthropy is clever.

And so on.

To sum up, at least somewhat, perhaps this may be the thing not to forget: The whole thing is nothing unless an attitude of some kind is imposed upon it, and the attitude most likely to impel fun appears to be that inasmuch as something or somebody is kidding something or somebody, why the hell shouldn't I, too?

A Soft Word
to the Gravedigger

A Soft Word to the Gravedigger appeared in *Cavalier* in September 1965. A year or two later it came out in the Weekend Magazine of *The London Telegraph*. It speaks for itself, of course, as in fact all of the pieces in this book do. About ten years ago in one of the big fat magazines dentists keep in their waiting rooms a long article appeared in which the theory was put forward that I had started out to be a good writer in 1934 but had steadily declined year by year. This was nothing new to me. Nor is it unusual for any writer to read that he is steadily declining. One might say it is unavoidable, because nothing is so convenient to the inept critic than to point out that the writer under consideration started out fairly well but quickly went to pot. This particular essay was accompanied by five or six drawings that purported to be of myself: in which the literary decline was revealed in the face, as sketched by a hired artist. The final drawing seemed to suggest that the writer really ought to be buried. All the same it continues to be my own theory that I am alive, able, willing, and compelled to write. And I know that the only money that has come to me since the year 1934 has come from writing, excepting for the three years I was in the Army, when my wages were something well under $100 a month.

Nobody is interested in what success does to American lawyers or thieves, but everybody wants to know how success destroyed every American writer who ever succeeded: Mark Twain, Sinclair Lewis, and Scott Fitzgerald, for instance, to name only a few.

There are specialists on this subject, and of course they prefer the writer to be dead, to have been knifed in the back by fate, or America, or money, or success, because then it is an open-and-shut case, as the saying is, and the specialist can get right in there and be very bright—and important, too.

He can say how he read Mark Twain when he was 11 years old, and again when he was 21, and still later when he was 31. He can say how he once spoke to Sinclair Lewis and called him Red, because calling him Red meant they were pals. He can say how he once wrote to Theodore Dreiser, asking him if he really believed his novels were as effective as action in the matter of social reform. And, in reporting that Mr. Dreiser didn't answer his letter, he can indicate how success had begun its deadly work on yet another writer. And he can do just about anything he likes with Scott Fitzgerald, who published a book called *The Crack-up*, in which he made it quite clear that he had had a lot of success but a lot of failure, too.

As long as his boys are dead, the specialist is just fine. His theory is proved, for what is better proof of failure than death? But let the writer still be hanging on, and it makes trouble for the specialist. He can dig a grave, but he can't put a live man in it. He can hope that by the time his writing appears in a magazine or in a book, the writer will have obliged him by dying or by killing himself, and then of course the specialist will have a scoop, and he will appear to be a prophet, too.

Now, all I'm doing is dying, and success isn't killing me, failure is, or at any rate failure and catarrh. It isn't easy to make an autopsy on a writer who doesn't know enough to lie down and die, who doesn't even suspect that success is slowly but surely killing him or driving him mad, or both, whichever is first or most, as the lawyers like to say.

Well, now, the simple fact is that I have always been just about equally successful and unsuccessful, both in my writing and in the spending of the money it has brought me. There is no doubt that on six or seven occasions I made more than enough money, but then my idea of enough is not very much like anybody else's. I have always had the feeling that being out of debt is enough, and on six or seven occasions I actually got out of debt.

Now, it doesn't matter that I hadn't gotten myself into debt on behalf of writing, or in a good cause of any kind. I hadn't had a bad time as a writer and I hadn't gotten into debt in order to buy a ready-made suit, a pair of shoes, or a beret.

I had gotten into debt from the old and well-established limitations and flaws of my character. I had always been both willing and compelled to use money as if I had a machine that made the stuff, as in a sense I did. I got into debt, I sat down at the typewriter, I wrote, and on six or seven occasions I earned enough to pay my debts again.

But I can't pretend that I have ever been as successful as three or four dozen other American writers, or perhaps as many as 300, including those who write for films and television. I have never needed to open an office, hire a business manager, call in a tax expert, sit down with lawyers, incorporate, reincorporate, double incorporate, and triple incorporate, and I have never gone to lunch with investment experts and discussed how to put my half-a-million dollars to work so that in a matter of five years, which would be passing in any case, the half-a-million would become two or three million, net, after taxes. I just haven't been interested in that stuff.

Every now and then I've overheard the really successful writers discussing their various financial coups and achievements, and I have almost admired and envied them, but I soon got over it, because they sounded like businessmen, and their writing, although enormously profitable, was no good. And of course the writing of any number of them *seemed* to be first-rate, but actually wasn't. I have tried to read it, to find out about it for myself, and the stuff just wasn't any good at all.

I've done well enough, I suppose, if you take into account that I used to sell papers and don't sell papers any more. And I have seen older men than myself selling papers, and they appeared to be as real and as interesting as any writer I have ever met, successful or half-successful or not successful at all.

My success has been different.

You might even say I have been successful in spite of the fact that I have always failed. I have always written what I *had* to write, such as this. What is it? It's not a story, it's not even a proper autobiographical fragment. It hasn't got a plot, and there aren't any big parts in it for any of the stars of stage or screen. For all I know, it doesn't have a chance of being published, even.

Publishing is getting to be something else, too, just as writing long ago began to be something else, too. A publisher isn't any more interested in writing for its own sake than a produce merchant is interested in potatoes for their own sake, or a manufacturer of cars is interested in cars for their own sake. What everybody wants is something he can sell, fast. And there's nothing wrong with that, either. I'll be very glad, for instance, if my next book sells a million copies in all editions, as they say, but on the other hand I won't kill myself if it sells only a thousand copies. Why should I? I'm a writer. There's plenty more where that came from. Now, if I won't kill myself from failure, I don't see why I'd be likely to from success.

But the gravedigger seems to look at it another way. His attitude seems to be that success is actually killing me (or any other writer he might find useful), and I just don't happen to know that it's killing me, perhaps from not having gone to Harvard, or from never having had any real intelligence; just an innocent slob being pushed steadily into the grave.

Well, I don't agree, that's all. I like writers. I like the successful ones, the rich ones, the incorporated ones, the good ones, the bad ones, the real ones, and the phony ones. I'm interested in the whole thing. I like especially the ones who can really write because they have got somebody to write out of, namely themselves, but there just aren't many of them anywhere in the world, let alone in America. Time and trouble catch up with writers, time starts to run out on them, they get confused, they get scared, they goof, they run away, they hide, they curse it all. I like them. They're fighting something.

The point is: I'm trying to remember what success actually did to me, and of course by success it must be understood that I refer to the success that the specialists mean when they speak about it: acceptance, fame, money.

By the end of 1939 I had all of these things, but I also had a gimp, and from having had to salvage a totally wrecked play, against a lot of expert opposition, I had become irritable, and frequently seemed arrogant and rude. But I did salvage the play, called The Time of Your Life.

It was the first American play to win both the prizes, and it did bring me enough money to pay all my debts, so I paid them. But there was still money enough left over for anything I might care to buy, so of course the question is what did I buy? I didn't buy anything. I only wanted that play to be the play I had written, and that's the play it became.

I could have turned that triumph into an industry, there's no doubt about it. I could have made deals with Kewpie-doll manufacturers, and sweat-shirt manufacturers, and distillers, and nightclub owners, and just about any money-hustling outfit in the world, but I didn't do it, and I'll tell you why I didn't do it. It wasn't my work. What's more, I was bored with the whole thing. There was other writing to do. There were other plays to write.

I didn't consider it a miracle that the play was all right. I went to saloons and drank and had fun, but I would have done that if the play had been a flop. So it was a success, so what? Was everything else everywhere else also a success? Everything was precisely the same as ever, so I went right on being the same cheerful psychotic I had always been.

But just imagine how much more cheerful and how much more psychotic I would have been if I had not been a writer at all. And that appears to be the little thing that the gravedigger seems to forget.

The only success that means anything happens when a writer becomes a writer at all. The rest is beside the point. Would any of the writers the gravedigger keeps writing about *not* have died? Would any of them have been something more or better had they not become writers? Who knows? I don't. I should imagine, though, that they would have died in any case, and would have lived their lives out in pretty much the same manner, only worse, most likely.

I am not a success, and success isn't killing me. I am a writer, and I am dying, but I would be dying in any case, and had I not become a writer it is possible I would have died long ago, so there's a big fat profit right there, and not taxable, either.

Good Old Goody Goody Godot

Good Old Goody Goody Godot was written for Goddard Lieber-
son of Columbia Records to put on the back of the album of the play
Waiting for Godot, as produced by Michael Myerberg, starring Bert
Lahr. You will find it there if you have the album. Samuel Beckett knew
James Joyce and helped him to get *Ulysses* and *Finnegan's Wake* the way
James Joyce wanted them to be. He is another of the incredible Irishmen
in world literature.

I have read it, I like it, I consider it a play pure and simple.

A charge against it is that it is crazy. It is, or it isn't, and one
way or the other doesn't matter as much as one may imagine.

The "mad" in art, if anything, is "right" rather than "wrong."
All great art has madness, and quite a lot of poor art has it, too.
The very making-over of the "real" by one man (not God) by means
of drawing, painting, sculpture, or writing is in itself an act of
madness. (I have purposely omitted the composing of music, because that act has been related to the "real" only in what is known
as descriptive music, which is only a very small part of the enormous reality of music.) If a writer isn't "touched," however well he
may write, he is a journalist. Even the best writers of history—a
study of theoretic truth in events and people—were "touched," and
there was madness in the manner in which they put their lies, or
their truth, together.

You will observe that your friends who most bitterly protest
that a work of art is crazy are themselves quite daft and dis-

organized, if in a very boring manner, whereas the maker of the work is quite clear-eyed, clear-minded, and a master at his work. The maker could make in another manner. Then, why does he make in a crazy manner? That question is the beginning of impatient scorn, or of decent study—the beginning of rejection, or the beginning of an effort to accept, if the thing made is not instantly irresistible.

Waiting for Godot is not instantly irresistible. It demands patience, watchfulness, courtesy, and even intelligence. After ten or fifteen pages, a reader is likely to be quite at home in the bleak and comic inch of truth which Beckett studies with so much intensity that it finally gives the appearance of being very nearly the whole world and very nearly the whole true fable of man alive in it— with women in the kitchen, or the boudoir, or in the pains of childbirth, or knocking their brains out in wild careers somewhere. In any case, they are not in the play, and they are not waiting. It is possible to give this a great deal of thought. I prefer to give it only a little. He may have forgotten. He may have meant this play to be only the beginning of a much longer work, in which the women would be along in a moment. He may have meant that one or more or all of the men are women, too, or that waiting is exclusively male, or always male-and-female, or entirely neutral. It doesn't matter. Fleshy women are all over the place in other plays for no better reason than none at all are in Waiting for Godot.

In the rollicking musicals the girls are there, but in Waiting for Godot not even the old women are. But what could he do with them? At best they would ask Gogo to come to his senses and go home—that is, return to a hovel in the world somewhere. But Gogo is home right where he is, which is nowhere, on his way to another, deeply longed-for, nowhere, sometimes called The End, sometimes confused with The Beginning, and apparently so confused by Gogo himself.

The lively, deeply sorrowful, loud, clear and desperate theatrical manner of Bert Lahr would appear to be ideal for Gogo. That is, for the American Gogo, for there have already been English, French, German, Italian, and many other Gogos, and there will be more of them in the future, including more American ones. There will be something special and unique in each of these Gogos, as there is inevitably in each person in the world.

Now, if you want to have an idea of the rich potential of this play, cast its five parts—Estragon or Gogo, Vladimir or Didi, Lucky, Pozzo, and A Boy—from among your family or friends. And then cast it with the most important people in the world. Let a big

Russian be Gogo. Let a big American be Lucky. Let a big English-man be Didi. And so on. But don't stop there. Cast it, next, with the wisest, most righteous, and most serene men of the world—the scientists, the poets, the philosophers, the men of organized religion, the men of organized labor, and so on. But don't stop there, either. Cast it with even less likely people—financial geniuses, television experts, advertising maniacs, men with not a spot of unsuccess to blemish their lives, fables, acts, and daring and cunning achievements. Each new cast will give the play a fresh dimension of humor and sorrow, for the simple fact is that in the midst of the horseplay of time-killing—the jokes, the puns (I hear it's full of them), the petty arguments, speculations, public speeches, essays at the achievement of philosophical systems of thought and action, discussions of discomforts and diseases; in the midst of these and other things—the play is deathly still with its own truth, its own mockery, its own despair, and the players can no more escape this stillness than they can escape their own in times of pain, fear, and total loneliness.

The play is about nothing. All is nothing. All comes to nothing. All is nothing from the beginning. Life is nothing. Death is nothing. Everything is nothing. If you don't believe it, don't, but even as you don't, you do, and you know this also is the truth. And for some reason it isn't shocking, it isn't painful, and it certainly isn't comforting, for which thank God. It just is, and in the meantime somebody is saying something about his shoes, or his sickness, or a half-thought of perhaps doing something or going somewhere.

I can't guess in which language of the Babel of them presently alive in the world the play is most likely to sound best, but I have an idea it isn't English, which is a literal order of language and calls for expertness in usage. I should like to hear it in the language of a primitive tribe of people, possibly somewhere in Africa, and in pidgin English, in which The Bible has been recently translated and published. The play itself is in fact a chapter in the contemporary Bible of course, as all true and new works are. The gospel, so to say, according to Samuel Beckett, and good enough. Whoever wrote Ecclesiastes put it only a little differently.

Does the spirit of it—if I may be permitted to use that word —suit us? Our time, our lives, our fables? Is nothing our true and just reward? Is wretched waiting for the inevitable the reward we have run so swiftly to seize, when all along we believed it would be something better? Is that all our reward is? In terms of this simple play, and in terms of the parallel reality of its truths in our own experience, it is, of course.

But this is not the only play, and if waiting is all we ever actually do, there are other ways of waiting, other ways to forget that we are in fact waiting, and finally other ways to give over to being seized, rather than to seize. The work is a play. Its best excuse is to entertain, and let no one pretend that it is trivial to be entertained, trivial to seek to be entertained, trivial to entertain.

Another charge against it is that it has no form. Well, form is a big order and it means different things to different people. To me the play has flawless form. It starts right there with the first word, ends with the last, and in between goes everywhere without taking one step, and back again. It has no tricks, and cannot be made into a movie for at least five years. By that time it will have been done at a cost of perhaps five thousand dollars by a desperate has-been in movie production, or by a brilliant young genius who is sure there is a big market for despair. In the movie, there may or may not be flashbacks to women, but chances are there will be. This won't hurt a soul.

Still another charge against it is that it doesn't mean anything, or rather that it means perhaps too many things, none of them clearly defined. Charge dismissed. It means what it means to whoever is watching, listening, or reading. What else could it possibly mean?

It is an important play, perhaps one of the most important of all, of all time. Nothing happens, but somehow or other a great deal happens, and none of it is strange, unfamiliar, unbelievable, or superdramatic. All of it is simultaneously delightful and annoying, laughable and heartbreaking, ridiculous and tragic—and yet nobody soliloquizes and then runs amuck killing father, mother, brother, sister, wife, son, daughter, uncle, aunt, cousin, friend, enemy, stranger, or passerby. In the other plays they did that, and it didn't help.

It is an important play because it reveals what else can be done in the theatre, on the stage, and suggests to cleverer and more skillful playwrights a little of the enormity they have denied themselves through expert adjustment to reality and the market.

I do not mean this unkindly, but it isn't very likely in my opinion that Samuel Beckett will write a better play. I don't know how he wrote this one, but I'm glad he did. It's really quite bad, but that's beside the point.

It also happens to be great.

Paint, People, and Mexico's Tamayo

Paint, People, and Mexico's Tamayo was written in Malibu in April 1954, for the program of a one-man show of the paintings of Rufino Tamayo. The name of the gallery is a famous one, both in New York and in Beverly Hills, and as soon as I can remember it I will mention it. Now, the thing about painting is that if there is a painter and he is not dead, getting high prices for his canvases takes a little doing. It's business, and can suddenly become big business. (Perls. That's the name.) But the real thing about painting is something else again—and not easy to pin down. Flawless skill at painting doesn't make a good painter, let alone a great one. And ignorance doesn't stop a painter from being great. The natural expression of Mexico is pictorial rather than literary. The country creates painters everywhere, and only here and there a writer.

Twenty-five years ago in San Francisco I was in and out of art galleries all the time, and whenever I saw somebody disheveled, discouraged, disgruntled, disgusted, and a little deranged-looking —generally loitering behind cash-customers in the hope of over-hearing a little sincere praise, or sitting on the exit steps thoughtfully eating a peanut-butter sandwich—I knew he was the painter, and invariably I sought him out and said, "Great. You've done it. You've really gone to work and done it." Once, though, it wasn't the painter, it was a fellow who like myself had come in out of the rain; but even he felt pleased by my opinion and believed he deserved it, as he very probably did.

I did feel, as a matter of fact, that each painter was great and had done it, and it never mattered that neither of us knew what the other was thinking. I knew I was thinking it was great that he'd gone to all the trouble and had put frames around them; while he was probably thinking of a more profound and purposeful order of greatness.

Now and then, though, a painter would *be* great, so that I wouldn't need to mention the matter; all I would need to do was look, whereupon he himself might ask if I thought well of the frame.

Which is how it goes, and by which I mean to say great is great, and somebody saying so doesn't help. (Does it hinder? I doubt it, but I may be mistaken.)

I went to art galleries not only to get out of the rain but to learn to write, for there is a connection.

The apprentice writer (painter, or human being) needs a city, the streets, the public library, the bookstore, the art gallery, the museum, the church, the market, and all of the other places to which the admission is free, the places of art and faith, or the places of the raw material of them.

In the days of the Depression my favorite hangouts in San Francisco were the art galleries, the public library, the Third Street joints, the Crystal Palace Market, and the Church of God (which was an empty store on O'Farrell Street just off Fillmore).

In the church I saw the human soul as Orozco might have painted it: I heard it sing wild hymns and speak in wilder tongues.

In the public library I examined only those books which could not be borrowed, the books of Art in the Reference Room; and the books of Patents, for there is nothing so instructive as man's foolish inventions, along with their preposterous illustrations.

In the Third Street joints I listened to the calling of the races, and watched the awesome running of them in the faces of the gamblers.

In the Crystal Palace Market I watched the hungry shop carefully for food, and I watched the food itself as if each small area of it was the original still life, as it was.

Everywhere I went I saw great pictures and I wished to God I could paint them, but I was a writer, and an unpublished writer at that. I knew one thing, though: if I knew how to paint, I knew I'd paint great pictures.

That's what everybody in the world knows he'd do if he could write (which he can't)—that is, write great books. But if the city didn't teach me to paint, it certainly helped me to learn to see, and it was by seeing that I may very well have learned the little I know about writing.

The best instructor of all, though, was the painter. When he painted greatly the whole world became more clearly visible; and whenever I felt I was missing something in the world, I would duck into another art gallery and have another look at another painter's stuff. If the stuff was good, I would know what I had been missing, and why I had been missing it. I had been missing the details, which constitute Art, and it was generally either because I had been moving too quickly or that I had been looking by memory instead of by use of my own very limited and possibly lopsided apparatus of optics. The good painter always brought care back to my looking, for the good painter is one who looks carefully, as if his breathing depended on it.

He looks at everything and anything as if it were Meaning itself—a fallen drunk on the late-night sidewalk, for instance, stepped around, hurt, heedless, hopeless, heroic, more than half dead, but at the same time indestructible; or he looks at a familiar street suddenly brand new but still in ruins; or at a fly on an apple, as if the apple were the World itself and the fly had come there by plan, with flag and reason and humor, a thing more marvelously designed and less useless than the latest unexploded nuclear bang.

As I write, I am looking at reproductions of Tamayo's paintings in a book, and everything I see, half-blind as I may be (not in optics so much as in age and ignorance), is man's own Art, and Tamayo's own portion of it.

He paints for the blind, and we are the blind, and he lets us see for sure what we saw long ago but weren't sure we saw. He paints for the dead, to remind us that—great good God, think of it —we're alive, and on our way to weather, from the sea to the hot interior, to watermelon there, a bird at night chasing a child past flowering cactus, a building on fire, barking dogs, and guitar-players not playing at eight o'clock, every picture saying, "Did you live, man? Were you alive back there for a little while? Good for you, good for you, and wasn't it hot, though? Wasn't it great when it was hot, though?"

Oh La La, or
The Shot Writer

Oh La La, or The Shot Writer is a joke, written at my home in Paris, at 74 Rue Taitbout, in 1961, to offer to the celebrated colossus of the film business, Mr. Darryl F. Zanuck of Wahoo, Nebraska, whose personal headquarters were at the Plaza Athané, while his offices were on the fourth floor of an old building on Rue la Boetie, presided over by Mr. Zanuck's aide-de-camp, Mr. Edward Leggwe, who during the war was, in fact, a Major in the Army, out of Hollywood by way of a place called the Motion Picture Center, at Astoria, Long Island. During the war Mr. Zanuck was much in evidence at the Pentagon in Washington where Brigadier Generals and Major Generals were a dime a dozen. Billy Rose, on the verge of being eligible for the draft, drew up a 300-page prospectus for the usages of entertainment on behalf of the stimulation of morale in the Army. This prospectus was so overpowering the Army instantly shelved it, and Billy Rose's draft board decided against troubling him any further. "I couldn't have a lot of half-wit Generals pushing me around," Billy said, but he probably needn't have fretted, for I remember Hollywood characters in uniform pushing a lot of Generals around, and Billy would surely have been able to look after himself. The art of the film is not to be taken lightly, but I have found it difficult not to notice that those who run the movie business, not just in America but almost anywhere in the world, are hustlers—clever, tireless, swift, experienced, friendly when they want something, ruthless after they've got it, and forever threatening to take legal action.

For years, since 1934, every now and then I have written a story for a movie. In the language of Hollywood such a story is an Outline. An Outline is simple enough and short enough for even the biggest man at the studio to read and understand. From the Outline a deal is made for the writing of the Scenario, or Shooting Script. Nobody took the Outlines I wrote seriously, perhaps because I couldn't take any of the big men seriously. Through the proper channels I sent the Outline called Oh La La, or The Shot Writer to Mr. Edward Leggwe, to process and pass along to Mr. Darryl F. Zanuck, but between them they wanted no part of it, so I let it go, and here it is. I think it would make a great movie.

Writers in America who are over thirty-five are supposed to be terrified of deterioration, but not me. I welcome the stuff.

My first book, for instance, was said to have been passable, if a little on the loud side.

Ever since, however, year by year, I have heard there has been a steady deterioration in the poor quality of my writing.

My third book is just a little worse than my second, my twenty-seventh just a little worse than my twenty-sixth. (The foregoing sentence itself is a pretty good indication of the extent and enormity of this continuous eating away of a mind which at its prime was weak.)

But why doesn't it bother me?

I haven't had a best-seller since my seventh book. Readers are reading other writers, and not one respectable critic wants to *mention* my name, let alone say something nice. Intellectuals (but don't be offended, I may be half-intellectual myself) consider my work out of style, not in the current any more, far afield, unaware, unconcerned about the holocaust of contemporary reality, indifferent to the corruption in the government at local levels, and scornful of Zen, a thing I know nothing about except that it is supposed to be helping people for whom my contempt is constant and open. Why don't they wash their faces and still be unique or whatever it is they want to be?

The intellectuals, if they mention my name at all, say that I had it in 1934 but haven't got it any more. Well, they ought to know, and I ought to try to get it back, I ought to feel I owe it to them, but I don't try to get it back, I don't feel I owe it to them.

I'm shot, and it doesn't bother me. On the contrary, I enjoy it. I had always imagined I was very good at deteriorating, and I have found every new phase of it a deeply satisfying confirmation of my hunch.

The newest phase is movie writing—for money of course, but of course I don't get any money. There seems to be a little something the matter with the movies I write that is not unlike the little something that used to be the matter with my short stories, novels, and plays. Jerry Wald, for instance, who knows good writing if anybody does, wouldn't go for the movies I write, so I don't even send them to him. Sometimes I don't send them to anybody. As far as movies are concerned, I just don't know the score. Even so, not long ago I gave it another go and wrote another movie. I thought it was very bad, but it seemed to me I owed it to the Tax Collector to send it to Darryl F. Zanuck, because he is in Paris, and that's where I am, too. But Mr. Zanuck didn't even send it back.

Here it is, exactly the way I wrote it.

I suppose I ought to kill myself, but I have this idea that I can deteriorate still more, and I want to see how I shall. I'll find a way, I'm sure.

Dr. Hector Bliss is an old man from Pawtucket, Rhode Island. For half a century he owned and operated "Doc's Hamburger Parlour" and was twice visited by famous people: Earl Stanton, a bit-player in movies who was on location in Pawtucket—Earl asked for two nickels for a dime. And Martha Beeler, Ed Beeler's unfaithful wife, who wanted a glass of water into which to drop two Alka-Seltzers.

Doc never forgot them.

"Stanton killed himself a week after I gave him change, and ten years after I served Mrs. Beeler, Ed killed her and was acquitted on the grounds that it was unpremeditated."

After forty years of conversation and hamburgers, Doc sold out to a grandniece who turned the place into a poolroom, with a horse book in the back, and Doc went to Paris with his great-grandson Errol, to be in a movie, like.

Doc is standing at the bar, sipping beer, in a place called Le Fishy, not far from the Sorbonne. He wears a Kodak, a hearing aid with a gear-shift, a loose wig, and false teeth. The big toe of his right foot, bandaged, sticks out of a cut in his shoe. His left arm is in a sling, and the index finger of his left hand is also bandaged. He carries a cane, talks all the time, and smiles a great deal, but without any real animation.

All through his talk are such words and expressions as voila, alors, pisht-poosht, which he imagines suggest that he knows French, which he doesn't.

Errol waits on the old man, who sometimes treats him like a dog, but Errol doesn't mind because nobody else ever took him to Paris, nobody else ever even *suggested* it, and also because the old man "is a whole show all by himself." Not to mention that whatever's left of Doc's fortune when he dies is to be inherited by Errol. Errol wants to be a famous abstract painter, or a famous concrete millionaire, or a famous faith-healer. He wants to do good, to bring happiness into the lives of the less fortunate all over the world, excluding Red China, "because they made their bed."

It's early afternoon, and nobody else is in Le Fishy: just the owner, the owner's wife, Doc, and Errol.

Doc is chatting in English with the owner, who can't understand a word and consequently must listen carefully in order to justify his head-nodding.

"After the first world war I made up my mind to see Paris some day because a lot of my best friends were killed in the war. I volunteered when the Kaiser sank the Lusitania, but they turned me away for punctured eardrums."

All of a sudden a mob of students, slobs, beatniks, beardos, and weirdos come into the place, and crowd around Doc and Errol. The owner and his wife go into happy action. The talk is swift, joyous, and wild, but Doc can't get a word in edgewise. His exposed toe is painfully bumped six or seven times. He is finally questioned about his bandaged index finger, and happily replies, "Oh la la, accident avec—is that right, Errol? Look it up in the book, avec means *with,* doesn't it? Accident avec—what's the word for Osterizer?" Errol tells Doc there is no French equivalent for it, so Doc whirls his right index finger around: "Osterizer, whirl, whirl." The student who asked the question goes away.

A woman places herself directly in front of Doc and orders a glass of wine, for which she tries to pay with a lottery ticket that cost 1,750 old francs, or about $3.50. The owner refuses. There is a big French argument. Doc insists on acting as pacifier.

"Will somebody please be good enough to step forward and let me know in plain English what seems to be the trouble here?"

A Chinese student acts as interpreter, whereupon the woman offers to sell the lottery ticket to Doc for only 1,000 francs, forfeiting the 750, and giving him a chance to win as much as 50,000,000 francs.

"I'll be only too glad to pay for the wine, please inform the lady," Doc says to the Chinese student, "but I'm afraid I can't purchase the lottery ticket, even at a reduced price, because I am on a budget. Permit me to introduce my great-grandson, Errol Bliss."

Doc pays for the wine, and he and the woman become friendly in a kind of speechless way. She holds out her empty glass, Doc gestures for the owner to pour again, Errol says, "But great-grandfather, what about the budget?"

109

"You keep out of this," Doc says. "A little wine never did a handsome woman any harm."

Doc and Errol go off with the woman, who shows them her small flat, and one of her daughters, who is so like Brigitte Bardot that Errol yelps when he sees her.

"Great-grandfather," he says, "let's just forget all about the budget. When in Paris do like they do. You marry the mother and I'll marry the daughter."

"This woman may not be a widow," Doc says. "Look it up in the book and find out the word for widow."

The woman *is* a widow, however.

Doc offers to marry her, but she says it won't be necessary, just so he's thoughtful, considerate, and generous in matters of money.

"I am, dear lady," Doc says.

The woman assures Errol the same holds for him with respect to her daughter, or for that matter with respect to any of her daughters.

Doc buys the lottery ticket for 2,000 francs instead of 1,750, just to let the woman know he's a sport, and the daughter sells another lottery ticket for the same price to Errol.

Doc and his great-grandson go home an hour later with ten lottery tickets each, and the following Thursday they discover from the columns of the Paris *Herald Tribune* that one of the tickets has won 50 million francs.

"I knew the lady was trustworthy," Doc says.

"Fifty *million*?" Errol says. "There must be a mistake."

But there isn't.

Doc and Errol examine the money, in crisp brand new French notes, and discuss how they are going to use it.

Errol wants to start a hospital in London. "In Mayfair, where the rich people are, because they're misunderstood."

But the old man says they are going to *think about* how to use the money. They keep their wealth a secret, but every afternoon they visit the widow and one or two of her daughters, for tea and lyric poetry, or at any rate laughter and giggles, and they pay for all favors with generosity.

One afternoon the widow weeps and says she is enciente.

"Who did it?" Doc says.

"You did," the woman says.

Speaking French, the woman is able to convince Doc that he *is* somehow the responsible party, but he is dumbfounded when the widow says she needs 150,000 francs for appropriate medical action. Doc tells her no, no, he'll do the right thing, they'll bring up that little child together.

"You have money?" the widow asks.

Doc is cagey, but he makes known that he has enough money for all practical purposes.

"What about Errol?" the widow asks.

He, also.

Then, will Doc marry the widow, and will Errol marry one of her daughters?

They will indeed, Doc says.

Doc and Errol move into a new apartment on the Rue Lord Byron with twelve bedrooms. One by one more of the widow's daughters arrive. Every evening the widow and her favorite daughter take Doc and Errol to a movie and then to a nightclub. Back home the other daughters are visited by many admirers, all looking for wives. Everybody is radiant with success, but after nine months the widow has not given birth to her child.

One of her daughters, however, begets a son, and the widow asks Errol to admire his child, but Errol says, "Yeah, but I married Annette. This is Claudine's son."

"No, no, my boy," the widow says, "it is *yours* and Annette's, believe me." Errol talks the matter over with Doc, and they agree it's all right for Errol to be the boy's father.

One afternoon eleven years later when they come back from a walk they find the whole apartment empty of furniture, and everybody gone, including the widow, the daughter, and the boy.

"I don't understand the French," Errol says.

"What is there to understand?" Doc says. "They're practical-minded."

Doc and Errol study maps and decide to travel some more.

That's it.

That's the movie I wrote for money, or rather one of six or seven I wrote, using up the better part of a full hour for each of them.

Result in dollars and cents: nothing.

In prestige: nothing.

And frankly I don't get it, because I don't see how the movie could possibly be worse, or to put it another way how it could possibly be more suitable for Vista-Vision.

I see suitable parts in the movie for the biggest names in the business, whoever they may be. With choreography—a ballet of the daughters, for instance—the production cost of the movie could

111

be extended to the point of banking anxiety, which in turn would surely impel an enormous promotion campaign: television appearances of the stars, newspaper and magazine interviews of the producers, photographic essays in *Life* about Marriage Relations Around the World, a controversy with the State Department about the kind of Americans in the movie, a sponsored attempt at censorship, with a consequent rallying of all freedom-loving liberals in the arts with the slogan *Oh La La Must Not Be Stopped.*

I have been out of touch with television for two years, but I have stayed fairly close to the progress of movies: U.S., English, French, Italian, Swedish, German, Russian, and Armenian. The outstanding thing about all of them is that they are earnest, and have no right to be.

This unintentionally comic earnestness is partly responsible for the enormity of my ineptitude as a movie writer, although I have no desire to put the blame where it doesn't belong.

I, and I alone, write my movies. I "see" my movies more vividly than I ever would be likely to see them were they in fact filmed.

They certainly constitute a tragic portrait of a writer in ruins. It would be sad, I suppose, except that I cherish my deterioration, and even take pride in the fact that it does me no good, just as if I were entirely in possession of my wits.

The Eye and Hand
of Dong Kingman

The Eye and Hand of Dong Kingman was written in Malibu in 1956 as an introduction to a book of reproductions of his water colors. I met Dong for the first time in New York in the late 1940s, long after we had been in San Francisco during the Depression but somehow had never met. I liked his paintings and tried to say why. Some of them used to move me deeply, as if to pity for beauty itself, and sorrow about the inevitable ignorance of everybody about the size of that which moves him and keeps him in his own small place. I myself paint many swift paintings before I have one that I rejoice in seeing, but I don't know how to say it happened, or why. Painting is its own language. Writing is writing and painting is painting. If writing can be about painting, then painting ought to be able to be about writing, but I have yet to see a painting called Mark Twain's Writing, for instance.

He looks at New York as no one else does—as no other painter, writer, composer, photographer looks at it, and of course New York is the world. That's where he is. That's where his looking at the world is steadiest. That's where he goes to sleep, and where he wakes up.

He really looks at the place, and he really sees it. Everybody whose business it is to look and see looks at New York and sees something different, perhaps new, perhaps important, perhaps special.

But I don't know anybody who sees what Dong Kingman sees, and I'll try to talk about it in just a moment. I've got to be very careful about it because in a thing like this it's easy to go off.

This is it, I think: he sees the world this instant, and in his glance, in the instantaneous and miraculous reality of matter and color, of living vision, of memory captured in the painter's great skill, he sees the world gone—forever. Not smitten to smithereens by silly explosives, not worn away by time and wind and decay, but gone forever in the very instant of its immediate reality—mixed, colorful, plain, heavy, but lighter than a man's soul, right there now and gone forever.

This quality in his city paintings is deeply moving, both delightful and sorrowing. We are not looking at a human face—eyes, nose, mouth. We are looking at the configuration and color—the mass of a place, a part of a city, a part of the world, that's all. Nothing of the human being himself is in the frame, and yet the picture in its entirety evokes The Human—gladly, and simultaneously with a stab of loneliness, longing, love, loss—irreparable loss—ache. The locomotive—what part of the soul, the heart, the hope, the memory of The Human is the locomotive? No one can answer with accuracy, but the locomotive just naturally *is* some part of Man. It is not a locomotive as a locomotive is a locomotive on a railroad, in the heart of a city, on the waterfront, or out in the plains. And this has nothing at all to do with such literal relationships as traffic lights being the equivalent of eyes, or anything like that. That sort of thing is trickery, and nonsense. Nothing in Dong Kingman's paintings looks like something else, something it isn't. It looks like what it is. It's the *way* he paints that makes the thing painted—a traffic-signal arm, for instance—evoke a spiritual condition out of common experience.

Now, it has always been inevitable for the skilled painter of landscapes to achieve a quality of man's soul, in one or another of its dimensions, in the far-off turnings of streams upon the land, or the lonely grandeur of grasses and trees, human paths, roads, places, dwellings, and so on. The skilled landscaper of nature evokes in his paintings as a rule a lyric, or almost religious, quietude—nature's own far-off aloofness, serenity, anonymity, universality, and perhaps even indifference. Good landscapes are always good to look at. They do the eye and the heart, and possibly the mind, a lot of good. I won't ever be willing to knock A View of Toledo, for instance. The clouds, the castle, the road, the wind, and the Greek's great skill are forever irresistible.

Well, here's Dong Kingman holding an eye on the jungle and clutter of a city—an eye that's both microscopic and far-seeing— here he is holding that eye on a small patch of a vast city, an in-

114

finitely varied world, and by the miracle of his great skill, here he is making asphalt and steel, stone and glass, brick and board and iron and tin, streets and buildings, automobiles and trains, junk of all kinds—here he is making all of these things into an entity that is instantly real, forever gone, and somehow immortal, as if in his junk is Man's monument, the image of his lost and indestructible soul. And this juxtaposition of rubbish and grandeur is just naturally beautiful. You look and you see, and you don't know why, but you're awfully glad about the whole business—man's proud futility, his brilliant failure, his heroic loneliness, his awareness of his end and his refusal to care about it. His refusal to stop in his tracks and let it all go. If he can't make a miracle, he can make locomotives. If he can't go to heaven, he *can* go to Hoboken.

He's an American, out of China, out of San Francisco. He's a wit. He tells some of the funniest stories anybody has ever told. His eyes twinkle with laughter and affection—for all things. All people. But never for an instant is he far from profound and steadfast earnestness. Perhaps even sorrow.

The Foot of Time, unpainted, without image, seems to be in each of his canvases. It is an enormous foot, vaster than the earth. It seems either to have just stepped upon everything, or about to do so. This Foot of Time seems to stamp the world as a side of beef is stamped by a Government Inspector, but there's no telling what the message is. Sometimes it seems to be The End, and then suddenly it's Forever, and then Now, and then The Beginning, and back and forth and all together, so that the sum of the feeling evoked is a mixture of New, Old, Ended, Started, Gone, Indestructible. Beautiful, and Tragic. And yet nothing he paints may be considered beautiful in any conventional sense. It's something, an assortment of things, made by man, seen every day, unnoticed every day, ignored, forgotten, much too familiar to be truly beautiful. But Kingman makes these things terribly beautiful. How does he do it? I doubt if he can say, and I know I can't.

The better part of any real work of art is essentially unaccountable. Still, it would be absurd not to understand that he does it by skill, by technical skill, by the skill of a painter. That is to say, he does a good part of it by skill—by eye and hand, paint and brush. The rest—the mystery—belong to art, to human experience, to Kingman, to me, and to all of us. We don't know how he does it, but he does it, and that's what we care about.

He makes his paintings in a studio, on canvases with paints and brushes. That's a fact, but there is another fact that can't be measured, weighed, or identified—the fact of how. How does he *really* do it? All great art appears to come from all men through one man. In one man it comes in one way, in another it comes in another. In still another it comes entirely from paint and brush, and you always know it, however cleverly the images and colors are arranged. There is a lot of good technical painting. There isn't a lot of painting that is good both technically and as art. Anything at all that is looked at carefully is worth seeing. Looking carefully makes it—whatever it is—a thing of fresh reality. The careful looking is the thing that does it. The act of careful looking, the event of seeing, is in itself the creation of beauty, and possibly truth, or at any rate meaning. But to look and to see, and then to be able to achieve the miraculous, the unaccountable, that is the rare thing, the deeply moving thing, and that's exactly what Dong Kingman does in his paintings.

How to Write a Short Story

How to Write a Short Story appeared in *The New Republic* in October 1954. It is another book review, containing a few more words about Edward J. O'Brien who died in London during the war, not long after I met him for the first and last time. Martha Foley took over the editorship of the annual *Best Stories,* and was later assisted by her son David Burnett. To me the short story is irresistible. As something to read, I prefer it above all other forms. As something to write, it continues to be for me the most inevitable and natural of forms.

When Edward J. O'Brien became a specialist of the short story in 1915 the world was a rather strange place. Unbelievable forms of imbecility seemed permanent, proper and even desirable. It seemed out of order even to *think* that anything wrong might be put right.

A writer with a soul like Kipling's was taken for quite a good writer because he *was* quite a good writer, and his soul was taken, or mistaken, for quite a good one, apparently for the reason that he wrote so well. A lot of his soul was in fact quite good, but most of it was bad, or at any rate unfortunate. He was able to believe, for instance, that an Englishman was superior to a Hindu, without particularizing either of them, but Gandhi turned out to be the superior of any Englishman of the past half century.

The writer is still up against this difficult problem. Can he heed his suspicions about big things? Does he dare?

117

In the U.S. there is much that is wrong that American writers for some reason are unable or unwilling to attack, or even point out. In fact, some of the most skillful and famous writers support the wrongs. It is difficult not to. One's friends are always such pleasant and earnest idiots that one is fearful of hurting them.

Most short story writers, most novelists, playwrights, and poets, could very well stop writing, could very well never have written, with very little loss, if any, to the health of man. At the same time every writer, however bad, has some connection, however unfortunate, with history and with man's health, or to put it more properly with *bad* history and with the perpetuation of man's ill-health. In short, if you write, your writing does something for or to somebody.

Here before me is the latest edition of *The Best American Short Stories*. At my leisure I intend to try to read the stories, as I am devoted to the form, both as a reader and as a writer; and because I am always on the lookout for the arrival of a new writer who may just turn out to be a little like Jack London, for instance, only better; a little like Mark Twain, only better; a little like Theodore Dreiser, only better; and so on.

Just glancing at the names in this book is heartening, for many of them I have never seen in print before. Maybe among them is a name that is going to stand there like a rock because it is the name of a writer who *is* a writer. The older names, in this book, or in the book of American letters, including my own name, are the names of writers who did, and do, pretty well, but failed, and fail—but keep trying, at any rate. They are the names of writers who are forty now, or older. Some who were young men not so long ago, one is a little surprised to discover, are now suddenly sixty; and many are dead, in body as in book. The writing goes on just the same. Collectively, gathered together, with the names thrown away, American writing is the best yet, if the most uniform, and lacking in greatness. This condition appears to be related to the arrival in man of the collective soul. Everybody's got a little of it, nobody's got a lot.

If you're a short story writer, your best chance to write a great one is to write with ideas and not with words, and for a better reason than to make a dollar or a name. Don't write at all, unless you would even if it were against the law, and would have to cost you every friend you ever had.

Fletcher Martin, Painter

Fletcher Martin, Painter is an introduction to a book of reproductions of his paintings. It was written in the middle 1950s and published by the University of Florida Press. I look at the reproductions of
his paintings in this book whenever I think I ought to. As certain works of
music need to be listened to when one is 20 and again when one is 30,
40, and 50, so must certain paintings be looked at again. As one grows
or changes, something happens to the works one has long known—some
become larger, and reveal new meanings, balances, complexities, or
simplicities.

I have forgotten when we first met but I know it was during
one of my visits to Hollywood, in 1933 or 1934. At that time
Fletcher Martin was in his late 20s. The thing that is memorable
about him was a quality of quietude. There was a touch of melan-
choly in him. He spoke slowly and in a deep voice. He seemed to
move with a pace that was his own. Everybody else I was apt to
meet in those days seemed to be in a hurry. He wasn't.

I think it was at Stanley Rose's bookshop that we met. If this
is not so, then Stanley Rose introduced us somewhere or other. The
three of us certainly got up before dawn one day and went fishing
near Malibu, because I wrote a short story about it, and while I
haven't looked at the story in a great many years I know it was
about the three of us fishing and not getting a fish.

At last a number of sharks came up out of the sea to look at *us.* This seemed to me something to remember.

In those days Stanley Rose exhibited paintings in a gallery at the back of his bookshop. I may or may not have seen some of Fletcher Martin's paintings on the walls of this gallery before meeting him, but I know that soon after we had met I did see a number of his paintings. I remember also, to sum up as quickly as possible the long ago, that on Friday nights for a couple of weeks Fletcher Martin and I went to the Hollywood Legion Arena to see the fights.

I remember that we paid half a dollar apiece, or as little as possible, to gain admittance into the arena, and that consequently we sat up high and far back, so that we saw both the fights and the people at the fights.

This is important to anybody who is watching things in general.

I remember also that at that time there were a number of very good Filipino fighters, one of whom, Ceferino Garcia, was famous for what is known as the bolo punch, and a refusal to be knocked out.

There were other excellent things to notice about the men in the ring and about the people who watched them.

On the whole, it was impossible not to notice that almost every superior fighter possessed, as if it were the quality which made him superior, a kind of instinctive regard for form, grace, and what I shall have to call truth. These are things all people in one degree or another must be concerned about all of their lives.

Now and then a very effective fighter would appear who lacked form and grace and apparently any sense of truth. Such a fighter very often won his fight—that is, destroyed the skill of his opponent, and yet impressed one as being a bum.

We went to the fights to see the fights. We went for the fun of it. But at the same time Fletcher Martin went as a painter, and I as a writer.

During those days I met a great many people, just as I do these days. A good many of them were painters, a good many more were writers, published or unpublished. I have never met anybody with an aspiration to paint or to write who did not seem to me capable of painting or writing. The fact that someone felt compelled to create meant to me that he *would* create. Making a thing is simple, but it is also mysterious, especially when the thing made is a work of art.

The depth of the mystery increases when the thing made was meant to be a work of art but turned out to be not a work of art.

Fletcher Martin was one of the many I met in those days who

was painting. He is still painting. I feel regret about the others. Some are dead. Some have gone away. They have left the arena. When I met them I believed every one of them would do great work. Living itself, survival itself, is not easy. To live, to survive, and at the same time to create is very difficult.

The probability of failure even for the lucky man who has survived, who has faithfully cultivated his skill, is certainly always great. It is, in fact, a miracle whenever anything he makes is a work of art. It is so enormous a miracle that when such a work is seen one is immediately humbled by it, and one is grateful for the existence of its creator.

Even so, I find that I have a special fondness for the failures, most of them by now forgotten, all of them gathered together into a single figure whose basic quality was earnestness. I have a theory that those who fail to do what they set out to do in art still somehow contribute to the eventual achievement of a work of art by another whose luck has been better.

Fletcher Martin's luck has been good.

I have only occasionally discussed with Fletcher Martin, or with any other artist I have ever met, problems of art. The reason this is so is that most painters and writers find that they are able to communicate ideas about art more effectively by speaking of other things—in short, by speaking of the raw material from which art must be created. That is probably why I began by speaking of the fishing trip and the prizefight arena.

Why any man becomes a painter no one may ever know with accuracy, and that may very well include the painter himself. The early opposition is so great that by comparison any other kind of work is apt to seem preferable, more reasonable, or even more meaningful. The contest of the unknown artist in the arena of art during the early years is a rough contest. It seems preposterous of him to presume that of all the people in the world he is the one who may, by the grace of God, create something that is real, that no one else in all the world can create. And yet it is this very faith, belief, opinion, delusion—whatever anybody chooses to call it—that a new artist must feel. He must feel that what he can do, no one else can do, and then he must go about demonstrating the truth of what he believes, thereby transforming what would otherwise be a crackpot into a creator. It is the probability that he may after all turn out to be nothing more than a crackpot that makes the going for the new artist so rough. The days of the unknown artist are long, tedious, and anxious.

I have myself from time to time for the sake of my own soul

sought to restore to my work this nagging doubt which is in the new artist. The reason for this has been that no man has the right to regard himself as an altogether professional or established artist. This is something others must take the liberty of doing for him. It is not, however, any of his business. His business is to look at the world, to re-examine experience, to go over once again, even if for the ten-thousandth time, the matter of what he thinks he is doing and what he believes he has observed about what other people think they are doing. No good artist can afford to presume or pretend that he has come upon final skill, final form, final grace, or final truth. If anything, he must remind himself repeatedly that in the matter of this strange creature, which is man, which has this mortal soul, there can be no finality.

There has always existed a great deal of interest in what it is that has been responsible for the arrival in the arena of art of a new artist. This cannot be explained, for the mystery of personality is the same for the good painter as for the poor painter. It is the same for the excellent bricklayer as for the slipshod bricklayer. It is the same for the man who endures time with grace as for the man who endures time without grace. Personality itself is the mystery. And while it may be in order to seek to unravel this mystery, or instructive to do so, it would seem to be an activity that is basically irrelevant.

I have never found it possible to be astonished that anybody has created a work of art. I have always believed that this is perfectly natural, that it is in fact inevitable. I have heard that somewhere in Southern Asia there is a whole nation in which it is taken for granted that every person is an artist. (Bali, I believe.)

Why the West has taken to an attitude of astonishment about the occurrence of art is something the specialist may very well be able to account for. I can quickly and inadequately account for it by expressing the belief that the peoples of the West have for so long been concerned with the picayune and the profitable that these things have become natural to them, but at the same time there remains in them a memory of a largeness of soul which was once their own; therefore when they behold this largeness in a work of art they are astonished and pleased, although sometimes they are astonished and displeased.

Adversity, wretchedness, unhappiness, want, neglect, disorder —these things, which are at best painful, may compel one man to greatness and another to something else—to simple, ordinary, universal humanity, for instance. There is no telling why a man becomes a painter of great paintings instead of a good farmer or a good printer or a good laborer. It just happens, accidentally and haphazardly—but that is also the way people themselves happen, so that this gets us nowhere, either.

If someone were to ask me, for instance, Why did you become a writer? I think I would have to reply quite truthfully, I had to.

I am sure it is much the same with Fletcher Martin. In any case, he is a painter, and I think a great one.

Among his paintings I find that I have a personal fondness for Trouble in Frisco, 1938; A Lad from the Fleet, 1938; Exit in Color, 1939; Temptation in Tonopah, 1940; Killer in Costume, 1942; Tuny, 1943; Boy Picking Flowers, 1943; The Picador, 1949; Arabesque, 1949. My preference for these is not, however, fraught with meaning. I am sure that were I to behold the others as they exist on the canvas in color, I would revise and qualify some of my choices. I find all of the drawings especially appealing. Study for the Death of Sonnyboy West, 1951, I like very much. Also Girl with Hand at Throat, 1951.

He has done a man's work. He is doing this work with earnestness, courtesy, conviction, and quietude. I find the dignity in the faces of most of his people irresistible and important.

He looks like a cowboy of the West of 50 or 100 years ago, but he is a painter.

Why not?

Confessions of a Playwright

Confessions of a Playwright was published in *Tomorrow* magazine in 1949, and tells why I decided in 1944 not to offer any more plays to Broadway, even though I continued to write them.

There are a good many writers who make no bones about the fact that they write for money. These writers generally fall into two categories: (1) those who actually write for money and have very little money to show for it, and (2) those who do not know how to write for money and have a great deal of money to show for it, but enjoy saying they write for money. George Bernard Shaw enjoys saying he writes for money. It is easy for him to say that. He is a rich man and most of his wealth appears to have come to him from his writing. It is out of the question, though, that he ever wrote anything because he hoped or believed it would bring him a great deal of money. On the other hand, it is inconceivable that he ever wrote anything which he did not try his best to make so irresistible in itself as to bring him an income.

In short, after the fact, a writer may truthfully say anything he pleases about why he writes.

There are two American writers whose fame in recent years has grown in a small and not especially significant area who betrayed (when I first met them) an intense preoccupation with the problem of writing in a way that would bring them riches. Both of them tried to write moving pictures scenarios, and one of them tried to invent a comic strip, but these efforts failed. They then acquired the view that they did not write for money because doing so was beneath them, and it was after the cultivation of this view that their fame began to grow. They are now fairly famous, so to speak, and they do not have very much money. They have learned to write what they must, they have discovered that this writing does not bring them wealth, and they are resigned to it. These writers, in my opinion, are no better than the writers who actually write for money and never get very much of it. That is to say, their writing is not any freer than the writing of professional hacks, and they are, as a matter of fact, nothing more than professional failures themselves. The subject of their writing is failure, and the tone of their writing is a tone of failure.

On the other hand, there are fairly good writers who are terrified of failure and consequently go about their work in a safe and sane manner, consistently turning out fairly good work which almost always brings them a fair amount of ordinary notice and a reasonable amount of money. These writers have yet to produce anything more spectacular than a best seller or a Broadway hit.

To sum up the point here, we must acknowledge that it is not impossible to write well and earn money; it is not impossible to write poorly and not earn money; and finally, it is not impossible to fail to earn money by writing either poorly or well. If this seems complicated, it is so because the matter is in fact complicated.

Some writers are ashamed of their reasons for writing. They do not want to admit, for instance, that they write so that they will become better known and thereby meet a great many more people than they would be apt to meet otherwise; or, on the other hand, that they write in order not to be required to meet anybody they don't want to meet. There are writers who are ashamed to come right out and acknowledge that, insofar as they know, they write because they suffer from inferiority complexes, or that they are chronically sick and write for therapy. Some writers are even ashamed to admit that they write to show off.

Now, let us acknowledge at the outset that in one degree or another every writer in the world writes for one or another or all of the foregoing reasons, as well as for many others. Let us accept that it is possible that a man writes for the most astonishing reasons imaginable, and let us not be astonished, for it would not seem to make the slightest difference why any writer writes. All that any of us cares about is what he writes. Now, let us say for purposes of timesaving that there is a writer who writes for the noblest of reasons—whatever they may be—and that his writing is noble. Let us say that he is a truly good man, truly eager and faithful, and let us say that his writing is of a like order. Let us say that this writer achieves truth gracefully and creates beauty meaningfully. Let us say that his work is simultaneously art and a demonstration of his personal acceptance of a profound moral obligation to society. Let us say, in short, that his intention is consistently good and that his effort to achieve his intention is invariably industrious and thorough. And then let us say that he is a playwright, and then let us look into his problems, and hear his confessions.

A writer of plays intends and expects his plays to be performed. Let us see what this means in our time, in our society.

A playwright in order to have a play produced in New York must be a member of the Dramatists Guild whether he will or no, as the saying is. What does this Guild do for the playwright? It deducts money from his earnings, and it receives money that is due him, and it sends him this money, after deductions. Sometimes the Guild takes a little time doing this, and sometimes members of the executive department of the Guild are on vacation when the playwright needs his money badly. The Guild does not help the playwright write better plays or any kind of plays at all; it does not give him $10 a day when he is writing a play and does not have $10 a day; it does not care what kind of plays he writes or what effect the overproduction of inferior plays is apt to have on the future of the theatre or of playwrights. The Dramatists Guild provides him and play producers with a Minimum Basic Contract, and this contract is extremely minimum, but absolutely not basic. The contract is very infrequently revised, and when it is revised it is revised in favor of everybody but the playwright. It is revised especially in favor of the Dramatists Guild. Here is a parent no playwright ever had, and yet no American playwright is permitted to refuse this preposterous parenthood. Let us be generous-hearted and let us say that the Dramatists Guild is a fine organization and that it does all playwrights a great deal of good. The fact remains that it is also an organization whose method is threat and intimidation. In my opinion, it is, therefore, an illegal organization. It has collected a great deal of money from my earnings and I haven't the slightest idea what it does with the money. I would like to know what it does with the money and I would like to object to anything it does with the money of which I do not approve. I have not yet heard of its ever having staked a needy playwright, or of ever having financed the production of a play, or of ever having established a national theatre or a New York City theatre, or of ever having lent a helping hand to established playwrights of other countries who are in need. I would rather not be a member of the Dramatists Guild as it now exists, and yet I am a member. Early in 1948

I resigned from the Dramatists Guild but when I began to make plans for the production of a play in New York it was necessary for me to join again because I could not arrange for the production of a play unless I was a member of the Dramatists Guild. No producer is permitted to produce a play by a nonmember of the Dramatists Guild. No member of the Dramatists Guild may permit a producer who is not a member of the Producers Guild to produce a play. What is this but a monopoly? Why can't a man write a play and have it produced by anybody he pleases? Let us say such a man is offensive. Why can't he still write a play and have it produced by anybody he pleases? Is it not permissible for a man to be offensive and still have rights?

I will believe the Dramatists Guild is a fine useful sensible organization when it permits me to join or not join, as I see fit; and if I choose not to join, will not obstruct my work in the theatre. I would be willing to donate 25 percent of my earnings in the theatre to needy playwrights if I were permitted not to be a member of the Dramatists Guild, and would not be obstructed. If need be, short of denying my family shelter, food and clothing, I would be willing to donate all of my earnings in the theatre to a fund for the establishment of a Playwrights Theatre. I sometimes bet the horses for money. I write because I am opposed to threat, intimidation, monopoly, unfair business practices, violation of civil and private rights, and for miscellaneous other reasons.

So far we have glanced at an aspect of playwrighting which is supposed to be favorable. From here on in, the aspects of the problem grow more and more unfavorable.

The agent. Here is somebody whose very existence tends to establish the fact that artists are idiots and producers crooks. The agent is supposed to find a producer for the playwright's play, and when found, he is supposed to see that the playwright gets a decent deal; but no agent ever found a producer for a play unless there was a play in the first place and unless a producer happened to think the play would make him some money. Not having written the play, the agent is not hurt when a producer says he does not think the play will make him some money. The agent is not hurt when he fails to find a producer for a play, and he does not pay a playwright 10 percent of his annual income because he failed to find a producer. He just sends the play back to the playwright. Agents are absolutely unnecessary, or only necessary for minors. If a play is good enough or seems good enough, a few producers are always eager to try to make some money out of it anyway; and if it is not good enough or does not seem good enough, no producer wants to try to make some money out of it anyway. I have heard a good deal about the refinement, the culture, the depth of understanding of certain agents. These are irrelevant qualities in him, I'm afraid: his function is a business function and all he is set up for, and the only excuse for him, is to accomplish the impossible: that is, find a producer and get magnificent terms for a play that is no good at all. If an agent wants to demonstrate his refinement, culture, depth of understanding or anything else of that order in the theatre, all he has to do is write a play which leaves no room for doubt. If he wants to demonstrate his usefulness to playwrights on the other hand, all he has to do is make a good deal for a bad play. A good play by its very nature makes its own deal.

The producer. Here is perhaps the most preposterous mountebank of the lot. He takes a lot of time picking out a play he thinks is a cinch to make a lot of money, and then, instead of respecting his own judgment and putting his own money into the production of the play, he rounds up a group of people called backers and convinces them to put up the money for him. He gets 50 percent of the production for being the producer, and the backers split the other 50 percent among themselves for putting up the money. If the play makes no money he has earned a couple of months of excellent pay, and the backers have items for deduction from their taxes. This man frequently poses as an artist. He sometimes goes so far as to affect concern about social reform, eradication of injustice from the affairs of men, and the political education of the masses; but he never puts his own money into a production. He just doesn't believe in anything that much. The producer (especially if he has had a prestige success) frequently believes in himself to the point of fantasy—but of course he does not believe in fantasy in the theatre. (Can't understand it.) He is quick to notice that the last act of a play is "hopeless" and must be rewritten, and he can tell the playwright precisely how it must be rewritten. I have on occasion accepted the theory that the third act is hopeless and that the producer has precisely the right scheme to salvage it and thereby transform the play from a nothing to a smasheroo, as Variety puts it; and then I have had to explain that I myself could not possibly write the new third act, but since the producer is so clear about it, and since his financial interest in the property is so great, perhaps he would do us both a favor and write it, and invariably the producer has declined to do so. He has remarked modestly that he is a businessman; he has been in business twenty-five years; he helped Knut Hamsun get a job running a streetcar when he came to America in 1910; he discovered Maggie McIntyre of silent film fame; he made a quarter of a million dollars in one year alone from the musical Hot Ziggety; he knows show business; only last night he was reading around in Hamlet, and there's a play for you; but he is not a playwright, he is a businessman, and the third act is hopeless and must be rewritten. Even a bad play by a man who is a playwright is better than any play rewritten for a man who is not a playwright. If O'Casey or Shaw or O'Neill wanted to tell me how to rewrite the third act, I know I would be deeply moved by their generosity, but I also know I would not rewrite it that way; and I know they would never take the liberty of trying to tell me how to rewrite it any more than I would take the liberty of trying to tell them how to rewrite the third act of one of their plays. Any producer would take that liberty, though, and then feel hurt if a playwright did not leap at the opportunity to pick up a little free education for himself. The producer takes his instruction from the backers, it would seem, and they take theirs apparently from the latest hit, however great a failure it may be in reality.

The producer is forever trying to camouflage what he is doing —that is, trying to make money—by trying to pass for an artist. But in a showdown he will reveal his contempt for that breed. He is frequently eager for the artist to write for him because he cannot write for himself. If the playwright is so independent that even with the promise of a hit and a lot of money, he refuses to make a business deal unless it is a business deal—that is, a deal in which the playwright, all flushed with the excitement of all that money, tries to get himself a very reasonable share of the whole production —the producer swiftly and effectively switches the discussion from the realm of business to the realm of art, and remarks delicately, "Now, I want to tell you my wife read this play last night, and I have a lot of respect for her common sense, and she said to me, 'What does this play mean?' She's a well-read woman and if she had to ask that question you can be sure other people—the public, in fact—are going to ask it, too." Pause. "What does this play mean?" The playwright's goose is cooked anyway, so if he's smart he will reply, "I don't know." That is a stock question of businessmen when they discover a playwright who wants to talk business. They never want to talk business. They're not interested in money. They want to know what a play means. As a playwright, as a member of the Dramatists Guild, though an unwilling one, I offer to all playwrights this stock answer to that stock question: "If you will tell me how much money you have in the bank and what it means, I will tell you what this play means."

The director. He is frequently a playwright, and I have little fault to find with him, although a good many of the mannerisms of the producer exist also in a good many directors, especially those who are not playwrights. The director is a conductor, not a composer, but there are few directors who are willing to accept this fact. Sometimes it is possible for a director who is not a playwright to stage a play as it was written to be staged, but that must be very rare indeed. I have never had such a director connected with any of my plays. I sympathize with the earnest director's problem, for he has no choice but to create, and it is not very likely that he may perfectly create that which the playwright intended. That is why I believe that whenever possible a playwright should either direct his own plays or be on hand at all times to help the director.

I know I have found a lot of fault with the procedure of getting a play produced, but there has been a lot of fault to find. The situation is in fact a good deal worse than I have so far pointed out. A new development—without a doubt the most offensive of all—is the tryout in a private home before an audience of potential backers, men and women who have money to invest. As I write, on the last day of September, 1948, this procedure has brought to New York over one million dollars worth of plays: revues, musicals, farces, light comedies, fantasies, and serious dramas. So far only one of these productions appears to be scheduled for anything like a reasonable run. This procedure is in monstrous taste, besides being impractical. It makes a beggar of art, and if the custom continues we shall certainly see more and more expensive productions whose sole object being to earn profits for backers must do one of two things: drive the backers back to stocks and bonds or remove forever from the presentation of plays all ease, all freedom, and all fun. To my mind it is much more reasonable for a playwright to enquire of a potential backer where he got his money, how he got it, how much he has, what he has done with it so far, what his purpose has been in accumulating it, and so on, than for the backer to ask the playwright to put over his play in the parlor. In short, it is more reasonable for money to go on trial before art than the other way around.

The Critics. There is little to be gained for the theatre in complaining that the drama critics exert a great deal of influence: they do, and that's the end of it. Few of the drama critics of the daily papers are, as a matter of fact, critics; they are reporters, and they are pretty good reporters. They tell their readers that a certain play has opened, and they say a few things about the event. Sometimes they talk about the plot of the play, if it has a plot, but almost invariably they comment on outstanding or inferior performances of certain players; the scenery is frequently described; the direction is discussed; and the effect of the play on the audience, and its effect on the reviewer himself. Rarely is the play itself, as a play, as an entry in the playwriting sweepstakes, discussed. This is understandable. Readers of newspapers are not students of drama, they are people who expect to find out if a play is apt to appeal to them, or they are people who somehow enjoy reading about an opening, just as many people who are not in society like to read about the goings on in the social world. The newspaper reviewer's job is to write a review that will attract and keep daily readers. I have seldom had a haircut in New York during which the barber has not included among other topics the current theatre and remarked, "I see where another flop opened last night." Few critics need to be taken seriously. Their standards are properly Broadway, or success, standards. They cannot be blamed for this. It would be silly for a morning tabloid reviewer to discuss drama seriously. But it is impossible not to take them seriously as judges, and, for good or bad, we must understand that every opening is a court trial. It does not matter that the decision of the judges is only the equivalent of yes or no, thumbs up or thumbs down. In the event that the greater number of the decisions are yes, everyone specifically involved is pleased and proud and does not complain that the decisions were reached haphazardly and came to pass in a most mysterious and accidental manner; but if the greater part of the decisions are no, then, of course, everyone specifically involved believes it is time to clean up on the critics.

I believe I am the only American playwright and producer who complained when a play was praised. Of course, I was willing to complain only by word of mouth, as the saying is. I did not write a protest, but I wasn't fooled for a moment. Just as easily as the critics had for the most part said yes, they might have said no, and they said yes most haphazardly and for the least pertinent reasons. The play was The Beautiful People, which I produced with my own money—$11,000, as I remember it. I personally guaranteed the play, and I had money gladly refunded to any who wished to have their money back—for any reason—no questions asked.

Is there anything sensible to be done about the power of the drama critics? It would appear to be in order to have the first performance of a play—the opening—reviewed by every practicing critic. As it is, the magazine reviewers see the second performance, and certain reviewers for certain periodicals with limited audiences see later performances, if there are any. This is a foolish procedure. The same performance should be reviewed by all reviewers, so that a reasonable consensus of opinion may be immediately available to the management of the play; and for the purpose of having the more serious critics in the auditorium along with the newspaper reviewers. The management should arrange with the weekly reviewers to have copies of their reviews as soon as the reviews are written. In addition to this, certain individuals who attend the opening should be encouraged to write short reviews of the plays, for use by the management if the comments are favorable. Who should the management approach for such reviews? I would go about the matter thus: every person at an opening would be handed, with his program, a card on which to write his opinion in one word, two, three, or as many more as space might permit. This should be followed by the person's name, age, address, profession, religion, political party, financial status, health, and opinion on the theatre in general. These cards would be deposited in one of many boxes placed in the theatre. The man who pays his way deserves to have his say. He is supposed to be the great critic anyway, and it would do no harm to make it possible for him to speak out at last. As the matter now stands, the theatregoer is a sheep which hangs its head and follows the goats anywhere they happen to go.

Under the foregoing circumstances, how may the playwright do his work, maintain his integrity, and manage to survive economically? I have already remarked that I sometimes bet on the horses. I should like to enlarge a little on this. Horse bettors as such are generally regarded as fools, and it is proper to accept this view without embarrassment. They are especially foolish if they lose, and more often than not they do. But the virtue to the playwright of seeking to exempt himself from the urgent need of money by studying the races and occasionally making a bet is this: that it establishes more swiftly than any other activity the essential irrelevance and worthlessness of money, whether the sums involved are enormous or insignificant. This, in turn, re-establishes emphatically the profound relevance and worth of art, of integrity, of pride, of indifference toward material success or failure. In short, it permits the playwright to work as hard as he is able to work on a play for its own sake. For he knows that while it is not easy, it is nevertheless true that money as such, as money, may be abundantly obtained by so simple a process as believing one horse among eight or nine will run faster than the others, and backing up his belief with a bet. By the same token, he knows that much needed money may disappear that easily, too. Consequently, money by itself is seen to be so nearly meaningless as to be unworthy of any broader identification.

In other words, betting on the horse races gives the playwright the contempt for money which money must have in order for him to go about his work of writing plays in a free, proud, independent and sensible manner. It does not matter if he loses or wins, or loses more than he wins, or always loses and never wins. What matters is that he discovers, as he could discover by no other activity, that money is simultaneously phony and irrelevant, however profoundly it conditions the behavior of man, distorts his real character, and upsets his life. This discovery is a basic requirement for the playwright, and for that matter for all men who are concerned about the achievement of meaning and right in the affairs of populations, nations, governments, and cultural systems. The one world will obviously be one world only geographically until the horse bettor's discovery that money is irrelevant becomes an accepted basic fact to those whose end in life seems to be to gather together as much of it as possible, whether individuals, corporations, or governments. Why, for instance, is it acceptable for a government to maintain a Department of War and not maintain a Department of Art? The Army and the Navy do not have to bother their heads, so to speak, about the cost in money (or for that matter in lives) of any project, however experimental or even impractical: they just naturally get the money, which again brings home clearly the horse bettor's intelligence of the irrelevance of money. No one, of course, has ever been able to understand or explain clearly why a government does anything.

The playwright, to continue and conclude, who expects to do his work with a free heart even though he has little money must simply arrange his life in a way that will permit him to survive pleasantly without very much money. He must cut down expenses and still live as extravagantly as the richest man in the world, or as extravagantly as he likes. He must do without but at the same time never want. If he does not even have the very small amount of money he requires, then of course he must think about the matter very carefully and perhaps do something about it. To beg in the street anonymously, as a man who is in need, I regard as more honorable than to beg in a parlor as a playwright. To borrow (from anybody) is also all right, for there is no man in the world who may not someday be able to pay all his debts. To gamble, however, is the best procedure of all, for it simultaneously reveals his contempt for an unsound and foolish economic system, and provides him with either a clearer picture than ever of the fierce role of money in the affairs of men, or with enough of the stuff itself to keep him going for a while.

What Makes
American Writing American?

What Makes American Writing American? was published in *The Reporter* in September 1956.

The writing of one people, such as the English, inevitably affects the writing of another people, such as the American, especially in the beginning. If recent English writing is useless to American writing, the older writing of England is still useful, and may never cease to be.

But when was the beginning of American writing? Opinions must vary. Facts themselves must vary, at least in how they are interpreted.

In my opinion American writing began when the unschooled took to the business. This leaves out Emerson, but not Whitman.

Leaves of Grass could not have been written in England, Wales, Scotland, or Ireland.

Whitman himself probably couldn't have written what he wrote anywhere else in the world. In America, European man had an arena at last in which hope could be limitless, and anybody with sufficient intelligence, energy, and ability was free to achieve almost anything.

The earliest outlet for the nation's drives was in inventions—mechanical, steam, and electrical. Some were practical and useful, although a lot of them were wild and comic, as if they were the work of men who might better have been poets.

There's no telling what doubts may have been in Whitman's heart about the kind of "poetry" he was writing and how it would be received. It isn't unlikely that he sometimes believed he was making a fool of himself, because even in our time even our best writers, whenever they hit upon a new order of writing which they feel they must pursue, have doubts about what they are doing, and what the critics and the public will think about it.

Whitman published Leaves of Grass at his own expense. It was an instantaneous flop, although Emerson hailed it in a letter to Whitman. Emerson might accurately have said the stuff wasn't poetry, but he didn't. And the fact is it didn't matter whether it was poetry or not. No Englishman, not even as unschooled one, could have written as Whitman had, because none would have been willing to do so; none would have been willing to be so likely to be taken for a lunatic.

Leaves of Grass was the beginning, or it came near the beginning, of probably the most unaccountable and complicated culture of all time, the American.

Poe, on the other hand, belonged to the world of art, but as a living American he had a tough time of it. It remained for France to recognize his genius.

Whitman did not belong to the world of art. Whatever it was that he wrote, it just wasn't in any of the recognized forms, and what he wrote about just wasn't understood to be the proper subject of poetry. As for his manner of writing, it was practically anarchistic. Whitman belonged to the world. He and his work were the same thing, as in the founder of a religion. If he was anything at all he was a personality or, if you prefer, a personage, in the European sense—a personage without any inherited, social, or economic right to such a designation. He was Whitman, pure and simple. He was Anybody become Somebody by saying so, which is the essence and meaning of America. He may in time be named the first true American—the upstart with great if impudent confidence who does something different that turns out to be more than merely eccentric or ill-mannered.

This ego push is by no means obsolete among us. It persists all over the place, in areas of potential magnificence no less than in areas of inevitable absurdity—from subtle discoveries in science to acts of attention-attracting for what is known as publicity. Whitman was a loner, as most Americans are at heart. He belonged to no school, and founded none. Lincoln was a loner. So were Wilson, Einstein, Lindbergh, Babe Ruth, W. C. Fields, Ford, Edison. And in the world of writing practically everyone we recognize as great, whether we like his writing or not, was a loner: Mark Twain, Ambrose Bierce, Jack London, Theodore Dreiser, H. L. Mencken, Sinclair Lewis, Sherwood Anderson, Ezra Pound, Eugene O'Neill, Gertrude Stein, Ernest Hemingway, Scott Fitzgerald, William Faulkner, William Carlos Williams, to name a few.

What do writers of a place and time contribute to the people of that place and time, or to the culture, so called, of that time and place?

They supply the people with their own fable, which they received from the people in the first place. In order to survive, in order even to fail meaningfully, a people must have a fable. The facts just won't do. History won't do, probably because it's a liar. The day-to-day newspaper, radio, television, and newsreel accounts of the people won't do, either. There's too much of the stuff and it's too raw. The writer takes this raw stuff and puts it into a new fable, or into a new variation of the one fable every writer writes in his working lifetime. He does it for money, he does it for fame, he does it for fun, or he does it because he's mad or half mad, and therefore must or bust, or drink himself to death, or jump, or shoot, as any number of good American writers have done. The best American writers probably began by being mad, and if they survived probably ended by understanding and controlling *everybody's* madness. That is probably the major contribution of good American writers to American life.

American writing today is still unlike the writing of other peoples. The simple English of the King James translation of the Bible appears to have served as a model for a great deal of this writing. That kind of usage of the English language is almost impossible not to approximate if a writer wants to be clearly understood and at the same time to say something generally meaningful, as a fable seeks to do.

This usage of language is carried to an extreme in the fable writing of Gertrude Stein, which at the present time is generally considered to be gibberish. Perhaps it isn't, though. Perhaps it is a kind of writing that will create an appropriate kind of reader, and when it does perhaps it will be noticed that the writing is both true and meaningful. I won't try to talk about the philological explorations of James Joyce because he is an Irishman and because I have not yet found the time to do more than read around in (with pleasure, I must say) *Ulysses* and *Finnegan's Wake*.

In addition to the true fable makers there have been others. I won't call them the false fable makers, for a fable is a fable; but the fact remains that for me Poe's fable making is phony,

O. Henry's is both tenderhearted and tricky instead of true, and Damon Runyon's, while slightly amusing in parts, is bogus both in its affectation of underworld speechways and in its unhealthy pretense of admiration for human monsters. On the other hand Ring Lardner never lied or cheated, and everything he wrote appears to be both superficially and profoundly true, and terribly amusing, if bitterly so.

The purpose of writing is both to keep up with life and to run ahead of it.

Right now American life seems to be badly bogged down in an anxious preoccupation with the achievement of security (for the future), and it can't be done, or shouldn't be. There is also enough cynicism in the people at large about themselves, their government, the workings of their political parties, truth in general, justice in general, honor in general, and so on, to constitute a kind of deterioration of the national character. Everybody appears to believe everybody else is a crook, or given the opportunity will soon become one. The miscellaneous petty clerks of the government certainly appear to believe every American citizen is dishonest, especially in the matter of reporting and paying income tax. Nobody in the government appears to be willing to recognize that taxes are too high to be paid in full, right down to the last literal interpretation of the nine million illiterate laws covering them. And of course the cynicism of the people about their elected and appointed governmental clerks or executives is frequently confirmed by the public airing of theft, lying, double-dealing, and other forms of chicanery.

Is this sort of thing suitable material for the writer of fiction —of stories, novels, and plays? Yes, it most certainly is, although it is difficult material to work with, and frequently in the end the unabashed crook turns out to be a new kind of hero—because writers are not district attorneys, judges, or jurors, and they tend to find anybody they write about at least forgivable.

The writing of a true fable is always a problem for the writer. He has himself to put up with in the first place, and then he has his material to put up with, to recognize, to accept, and to work with. How do you do it? It isn't easy, and after a writer works very hard for twenty or thirty or forty years, he may still discover that he has missed the bus.

To sum up this aspect of the matter, I'm afraid we must face the fact that America is no longer new, that it has been captured and hog-tied by the rest of the world.

Is it in order for us now to get uncaptured and untied, or is it in order to abandon all illusion and theory of difference from other peoples? I don't know, but my guess is that it ought to be about fifty-fifty. We are captured, no doubt about that, or we wouldn't have condescended to be so courteous to the Russians, though God knows we might have been twice as courteous for better reasons than that we were intimidated into it by weapons that have got us all thinking of future security instead of heaven. In a sense we've captured ourselves. Insofar as that is true, it is in order to get uncaptured, but not in order to return to being discourteous to the Russians, or to anybody else. Just for the sake of our own souls.

As for being different, I continue to believe that at our best we are. This does not mean that we are superior. Nobody is superior to anybody, and if Americans can't understand that, they ought to go back where they came from, as the silly saying is. Only the superior are superior to the less superior, and both are about equally distributed everywhere, and who's who is immaterial for all practical purposes. We are different in our land—in the geography of where we are. It's as simple as that. When Detroit has stopped making automobiles forever, we will still be different in our land and geography. We are different to the extent that all peoples in all places are different, and after that we are the same, except for the jokes we tell and the fables our writers write and we read. Most of the fables are false, God help us—including some of my own. (But I needed money at the time, I was fat, the tax collector had liens out wherever I might hope to earn an honest dollar, most of my contemporaries were either dead or retired and the others had settled for the big money of movies or television, and I forgot to duck. Otherwise, my fables were true, and might have gotten at least more skillfully useful with time. As it is, I have in mind a new novel, a new play, and a new story that I think may be pretty good.)

How much do any of us need writing at all? Because of the arrival of the television screen in the American parlor a lot of earnest people, including writers, believe the need of the book is swiftly diminishing and may in time disappear. I consider this theory nonsense, not because writing is my profession but because there is no other language than the written one. Talk is O.K. for saying hello and good-bye, but after that everything must still be written. It can't be put on film in photographed images of truth or untruth. It can't be put into sounds, whether of alarms or music. It can't be put into odors, or in objects to reach out and touch, as the blind do at their schools, in sculpture, or in paintings, or in gadgets. We achieved written language in the first place because we couldn't keep very much in our heads.

Instead of the disappearance of writing, I have an idea that the time will come when print will appear on television screens—without noise or music or anything else: just clear easy-to-read print, the print of written works. A new book will be released as a new film is released. If it's for kids, the print will be accompanied by a clear voice speaking the words. The picture to behold will be print, not mice acting like people.

Still, the matter of television is not unrelated to the problem of writing. Even the television advertisements of money, spelled m-o-n-e-y, are written before they are spoken or acted out.

And of course there is a new order of writer at work in television. Let us put this as plainly as it deserves to be put: The television writer is a bad writer. He has his excuses, as everybody does, but this writer is the worst. Working under pressure, his easiest way to drama, when he writes plays, is hysteria. People on their way to the kitchen faucet for a drink of water are liable to stop in the hall and scream that they're unhappy because Mother believes in marriage rather than something else. As for the television directors, they are so good at hysteria that even when they get a play without any, they put some in. And nobody busts out laughing at the nonsense until Sid Caesar or Red Skeleton does it.

The lazy appeal of television may in the end do no more harm than to give the already split national personality a few extra splits, each fragment addicted to its own order of comfort—the book split, the newspaper split, the movie split, the radio split, the television split, the earning-a-living split, the bill-paying split, the children-rearing split, the baseball split, the sick-in-bed split, the sick-on-the-feet split, and finally the little split that nothing can touch, except perhaps truth.

Where is American writing succeeding? Where is it failing? For the most part, it is succeeding where the writing concerns itself with man as a sick bug, which he isn't. It is failing in what it isn't noticing, and in not employing a number of other ways to write about anything, or everything.

The most meticulously skilled writers, especially among recent arrivals, write brilliantly sick stuff, while writers with both skill and humor write plot or action stuff. Is the sick stuff so well written because everybody is in fact sick? I doubt it, because even the sickest man, the one in his last bed and not far from the end, is still also healthy. A farmer in Fresno once fell into an open manhole. The emergency doctor who reached him a few minutes later said, "How are you?" The farmer said, "Fine, thank you, Doctor," and he died. Or so the story goes. A joke of course, but it suggests what

139

I mean. There's something about sickness that's getting away from the doctors and everybody else.

In writing, sickness ought to be the healthiest thing in the world. There appears to be a little too much hate and self-hate in too much contemporary American writing that is otherwise quite good. And there is certainly too little humor and health in too much skillful writing that isn't enough concerned with the troublesome aspects of the human experience.

To sum up, the young writers aren't young, and the old writers aren't old. The young ought to be profoundly earnest, if a little wild and mischievous, and the old ought to be wise and funny. The writer, old or young, can't invent the American world, but he can look at it in one of six or seven ways, and he ought to choose the way that makes the best possible sense. On the whole, the American world is presently a badly mixed-up one, and that can drive a good man to a very small corner of the nation, where his material is a little less hectic and a lot more easy to work with.

A Few Answers
About Television

A Few Answers About Television was written in December, 1953, in Malibu, in reply to a long questionnaire from a big New York newspaper, for which there was no payment, so I didn't return the questionnaire. Why should I? If I sent *The New York Times* a long questionnaire about my writing in relation to the government and the stock market, I don't think they would fill it out and send it back.

Bad television has done nothing to bad movies, except bring them into the home.

Good television has worried the makers of good movies because good television doesn't cost anything to see.

Excellent television and excellent movies are the same thing—that is, excellent.

What ought the movies to do about television?

If by "the movies" is meant "the money," then the logical thing for the movies to do is to buy the television chains; but of course the procedure could be reversed and remain precisely as boring.

If an art form is meant, then the thing to do is meet the aesthetic competition.

The art form of the movie is the only form the movies have: it is their all, so to say, supplemented lately by movie-theatre lobby peddling of popcorn, ice cream bon bons, and soon no doubt shoelaces, toys, cosmetics, palm-reading, drugs, quick lunches, picnic boxes and subscriptions to the Encyclopaedia Britannica.

The movie art form, on the other hand, is not one-tenth of the excuse for television—which is without a doubt the most useful achievement in communication the world has known.

In addition to the movie art form, television carries free of charge to any who wish to look, among other things, the following: sports (while they are taking place), daily news, public and national events, including Senate and Congressional Investigations: trials, discussions, debates, ceremonies—in short, the whole simple and complex pageant of man struggling with his doubts, delusions, anxieties, hopes, fears, fantasies, desires, and demands.

The potential for television is limitless—solely as the means by which interesting things are made visually and audibly available to people at large, or in general.

The movies had better not try to do anything about this. They had also better not try to devise a means by which to muck up the free use of the television dial with slots into which coins must be dropped before the people may look at something and find out for themselves if they want to go on looking.

This coin-in-the-slot scheme is by way of becoming the grand larceny conspiracy of the age. It might have been launched, for all its cunning, by the polite and refined underworld.

Insofar as television is to be concerned with the art form of the movie, television must learn from the movies, and not the other way around. Television may have to go into the business of making movies—to show free of charge.

Live TV shows just haven't worked, that's all: certainly not when the show has been a play which presumed to be a work of art.

The playing area is much too small and nobody seems to have time for the fine points which finally, accumulating, constitute art, as against a miscarriage of it. Art directors, not TV directors, are needed.

As it is, catch-as-catch-can, television's achievement is already considerable, and little children have moved forward in only a few years from good-doing, phony cowboys and steel-faced space and light-ray daredevils to jovial Italian or Jewish chefs preparing stuff to eat or earnest men gathered around a table to discuss matters relating to civil liberties.

In short, they have learned to distinguish between the not-especially appealing fraudulent and the not-especially entertaining real, and to prefer the latter, or certainly not to reject it entirely.

The achievement of any art is difficult—because to achieve the exact, exact pains must be taken—but the achievement of theatrical art is the most difficult of all, even by experts.

Contemporary experts, for instance, are bogged down in their own particular *kind* of expertness—so much so that they are unable to cope with an unfamiliar important work.

Most television drama is based upon phony excitements, dangers, dilemmas, risks, probabilities, pursuits, and so on, with the result that the human race of these dramas is a phony race. Certain programs are even named after the spurious excitements they peddle: suspense, danger, and so on. They could do as well with disease, delirium, decay, derangement, or just plain death; or on the other hand, if it weren't just a little more difficult, delight.

But there is no need for alarm. All is well. The discovery of the alphabet, the evolvement of language, the invention of the printing press, the means to publish great numbers of books are one thing, and writing is another.

The flawless working of the machines does not compel a high order of writing.

The excellence of cameras and photography does not make moving pictures that are art.

The technical excellence of television doesn't in itself give everybody something better to look at than a sky.

But these things help. We have to be thankful that they do. (And then if we happen to be in a position to do so, we have to try to help them to help.)

There is no quarrel between the movies and television. They are part of the same thing. Television just happens to be the better part of it.

The Unknown Soldier
Identified

The Unknown Soldier Identified is a book review, written a year or two after the book came out. I sent it to a couple of liberal magazines, but they sent it back, so I let it go.

Eddie Slovik was born in February 1920. He was murdered in January 1945. Eddie was real, but like many real people his reality might never have been noticed had somebody not written about him.

Now that William Bradford Huie *has* written about him, Slovik is as good as imaginary, an odd character in an odd work of fiction.

The character is killed for claiming to be a coward, but it is this very claim that makes him the hero of the story.

Slovik put his claim in writing and handed it to The United States Army, of which he was a drafted Private. The claim struck other soldiers in the Army, from Privates to Generals, as preposterous, and Slovik was urged to renounce it. This he refused to do, transforming confused suspicion into annoyed hatred, and compelling the Army to spend a lot of time and money meeting the defiance with a formal trial.

At the trial, though, Slovik made matters even more difficult by pleading not guilty, and then refusing to say anything in his defense.

This was too much for his judges, including two dentists. They voted to have him shot.

Most of the judges told Huie many years later they hadn't

believed he would actually *be* shot, though, because no American soldier had been shot for desertion since 1864, although a great many of them had been tried and found guilty and condemned to death.

A General, however, had *not* doubted that Slovik would in fact be shot, no matter what the statistics happened to be, and it was his earnest opinion that Slovik *ought* to be shot.

When the time came, Slovik hated nobody and urged the members of the firing squad to aim true. The squad failed, though. Not one of the eleven shells struck the target, his heart, so that he was plainly seen to struggle up at least twice. An Army doctor applied the stethoscope to his chest. "His body was quivering slightly."

This bungled administering of punishment created an ugly atmosphere. The Officer in charge of the firing squad, remembering the written rules of the procedure, gave the order to reload, whereupon the Chaplain "spoke curtly" to him, saying, "Give him another volley if you like it so much!" The Doctor said, "Take it easy, Padre, none of us is enjoying this." Then, "While the young lieutenant was reloading the rifles," it was noticed that in his haste and nervousness he was pointing the rifles directly toward the enlisted-men witnesses. In a voice that few could hear a Colonel said, "Be careful, Lieutenant. Let's not kill one of our own men *accidentally* here this morning."

By the time the rifles were reloaded the Doctor was able to say, "The second volley won't be necessary, Major. Private Slovik is dead."

Was he killed accidentally, or on purpose?

And wasn't he "one of our own," too?

He certainly wasn't anybody else's, although he *did* feel that he belonged to Antoinette, his wife, whom he had married after spending five years in jail and for that reason had been classified 4-F. With Antoinette he'd had one year of home-making, furniture-buying, home-cooking, love-making, movies, beer, and plans for the buying of a private home, a car, and the raising of children—but not the way his mother and father had raised *him*.

He certainly never seems to have felt that he belonged to his father and mother, although he took his girl to their house and invited them to the three-day wedding, which they attended, along with his two sisters and a lot of other relatives and friends. His jailers were invited, too, but were able only to send telegrams wishing him happiness and good luck. They liked him, and he liked them.

During Basic Training in Texas he longed to go back to jail, and as a Replacement in France it was this longing that helped him make up his mind to get his preferred place in the living world established once and for all: civilian jail or military jail—if that was the only way to get back to Antoinette. The child she had miscarried during the first months of their separation needed to be put back, he felt. And the new furniture they had bought (like the kind in movies) needed to be used and enjoyed, especially his side of the bed, which he begged her not to let anybody else use—meaning his own sisters, when they visited Antoinette—because that place was his place: it was where he had come to the only good luck of his life, he said, and where he had found the cold feet of his woman and had warmed them with his own.

William Bradford Huie worked hard to get this strange, tender, and sickening story of Eddie Slovik told. At first the Army was against it, and then suddenly (after arguments by Huie) the Brass said O.K., and Huie took off. He met everybody who had known Eddie Slovik, and began to put the pieces together. Antoinette handed him the letters Slovik had written her at the rate of one a day, sometimes as many as five. Portions of some of these letters are part of Slovik's story, as told by Huie, who notices that while Slovik repeatedly refers to an unidentified "they" as if to an unnameable personal enemy, Slovik himself had no enemy among people he had met, and everybody (or almost everybody) remembered him as an earnest, kindly, unsmiling, good-looking Polish-American boy who was never too busy writing letters to Antoinette to do somebody a favor. He cut one letter short in order to hurry to the hospital to see a pal. In France he rescued a German flier from a mob, got him to safety, and didn't feel that the German flier was an enemy. Slovik and his pal, another Polish-American from Detroit, were supposed to take turns staying awake during the night, in order to watch the German, but they just couldn't play the game. They fell asleep, and it was the German who woke them up in the morning.

Huie got to everybody, or tried to, but he didn't get to the German flier. Perhaps the flier himself will some day add his piece to the puzzle—although it isn't really a puzzle at all.

Eddie Slovik began to go to jail as a kid. His biggest crime was the embezzlement of bread, candy, chewing gum, and small change worth a total of less than $75 over a period of six months. He got along well in jail. The theory was that beer and bad companions got him in trouble all the time. It's as good a theory as any, but useless, too. Huie doesn't bother too much about Slovik's father and mother, and doesn't appear to have spent much time with them

146

talking about their son, which is probably just as well. But Huie's idea is to account for Slovik, and then to account for the Army, Slovik's trial, and his execution.

There is no apparent effort to account for the war, perhaps because it can't be done.

But Slovik himself, finally, remains unaccountable, too.

The first time Slovik "deserted," he was one of a dozen replacements traveling by truck to a famous but hard-luck infantry outfit at the front in France. The group ran into "war," dug foxholes, got in them, and waited. When the war "stopped," Slovik found that he and his Polish-American pal from Detroit had been left behind. They were adopted by a small mobile Canadian outfit and spent six weeks with them, driving their own vehicle, stealing potatoes and making Polish potato pancakes for the Canadians, finding beef, and improving things in general for them. The Canadians hated to see them go.

The second time Slovik "deserted," there was no "war." Slovik simply asked an officer about the rules of desertion and was told the rules: if he walked away he would be classified a deserter.

Slovik began to walk away.

His pal from Detroit begged him not to, but Slovik said he knew what he was doing.

Having walked away, having "deserted," Slovik walked back several days later, and handed his "confession" to a cook, who gave him some food.

Slovik had "closed with the enemy" at last, and the enemy was "they"; the organized, all-powerful, unnamed, unidentifiable human machine of wartime law and order: American, German, Russian, universal, capitalist, fascist, communist, or any other kind. But Slovik lived in Slovik's Detroit and Slovik's dream, in Antoinette's basement apartment and bed, under Slovik's law and order. And he did not live in the war-mob or under its law and order. Everybody he knew he knew personally, and liked, including even his judges and executioners.

Before his trial Slovik was "examined" by an Army psychiatrist whose brief report stated that Slovik was in his right mind, was not mad, and there did not seem to be any reason to believe he had been mad when he had fallen behind the first time and had walked away the second. Slovik hadn't ever gone to psychiatrists of his own free will. During the seventeen weeks of basic training in Texas he had put up with everything reasonably effectively, although he goofed on the firing range again and again, and skipped a company beer party in order to write to Antoinette, because she and he were working on getting him discharged, and he had come to believe his discharge was imminent. Hadn't he signed an official-looking document in three places? Hadn't the Red Cross sent one of its Women to interview Antoinette, now sick, unemployable, and subject to epilepsy seizures again, from anxiety? The Woman had not liked Antoinette, and had urged her to sell the new furniture, move out of the apartment, and live in a furnished room on her allotment from Slovik. She in turn had asked the Woman, "What will Eddie think? What will he come home to?" The Woman said, "There's a War."

On a 26-mile hike with full pack in Texas his little toe took a beating, but he didn't see the Medics about it. The only person he could mention the little toe to was Antoinette. But then he mentioned *everything* to her. He called her Mommy.

Had he ever *needed* the help of a psychiatrist? It would appear that he had, if *anybody* ever had, but being a Roman Catholic it may never have occurred to him.

"I'm unlucky," he says many times, and Antoinette says, "Nothing good ever happened to that kid."

Nothing, that is, except Antoinette, nothing *until* Antoinette, five years his senior, his girl, his wife, his mother, his boss, his inspiration to go straight and be somebody.

The psychiatrist in France was quick about Slovik. He said Slovik was O.K., apparently only determined to avoid hazardous duty, injury, or possible death. Had Slovik shot off his big toe with the rifle he had sworn to himself never to fire at another human being, he would have been hospitalized, honorably discharged, and perhaps even decorated. Thousands of enlisted men had done that, and Slovik surely knew they had. The difference between them and Slovik was unique. Slovik didn't want to have the enemy fire the gun in *his* hands upon *his* foot. He wanted to wage and possibly win his war according to the rules: it is against the rules to desert: if you desert, you are taken out of your outfit and put in jail, you are tried, and you are punished. You might get twenty years, but after the war, "they" might let you out in six months, or a year. You will have been an "official" coward, but you will not be dead in France or Germany, you'll be alive in Detroit, and the stuff the war was supposed to be about will seem faraway and a little more confused than ever.

Slovik was offered a deal by an officer: go to the front line, and the desertion will be forgotten. This appears to have been a routine offer in such cases. Many men were glad to accept it. Slovik had no use for it at all.

"Try me," he said in effect. "I'm a coward. I ran away. Put me in the line again and I'll run away again."

This last remark concluded his confession, and he printed it in big letters. He didn't want anybody to misunderstand, and nobody did. He refused to be a sneak about it, to be clever, to play the Army game, to achieve the same end by an acceptable means. It was this simpleminded (or profound) directness that proved to be too much for his officers, too much, that is, for the Army of the United States, the government of the United States, the people of the United States, and perhaps for that matter the people of the world.

You simply cannot have what you want simply because you want it. You can have it only if you are willing or able to pretend that this thing in itself is not the important thing, not the thing you really want.

But Slovik's lack of cleverness appears to have been taken to be the greatest cleverness of all, a profound rudeness to everybody else in the Army.

He was shot and killed.

The Chaplain who attended him believes it was Catholicism that enabled Slovik to walk to the stake, to suffer himself to be tied to it, to have the rules and reasons read to him, to have the black hood placed over his head, and to wait for the inaccurate volley of shots, which surely proved the accuracy of his lifelong theory of personal bad luck. He certainly must have known in the last two or three minutes of his life that he might have done a little better in the rejected front lines.

There is something enigmatic about Slovik's whole personality, as it is revealed by Huie's chronicle, by Slovik's letters to his wife, by the comments about him by those who knew him, trained with him, shipped with him, judged him, condemned him, and killed him. He is a nonentity no less than the others, including the Generals, but he is a very young one, and there are enough flashes of hard, stubborn and witless straining in him after identity and meaning to compel a valid speculation about his short life and brutal death.

Was he the best man of the lot? Perhaps even the best American? Was he, perhaps, the Unknown Soldier himself, identified at last? Officially identified as a deserter, a coward, and a criminal? But unofficially the last soldier of the old theory of war, and the first of the new—the unarmed soldier in the unarmed war, the private citizen who is unable, even at the cost of his life, to forfeit his privacy to any idea, however unprivate and grand or heroic-appearing?

History and science may find it intelligent and useful to examine the Slovik Case again and again, beginning with his father and mother, his home, the employer from whom he embezzled a few dollars' worth of candy and coins, the Reform Schools and jails he lived in, the draft board and its members, the officers who trained him, the doctors and dentists and psychiatrists, but most of all the enemy, whom he, Slovik, found no different from anybody else he ever met, whom he befriended, in whose presence he was unable to feel fearful of his life.

The implication cannot be that Slovik himself knew who he was or what he was really doing in refusing to fire his rifle or to suffer himself to be walked to the committing of any murder other than his own at the hands of his own people. But that is the very reason he may grow to be the most heroic figure to emerge from the old theory of war, which is swiftly petering out as a means by which to achieve any kind of identity or meaning for any private individual or any gathering together of millions of private individuals into any entire nation.

Applause

Applause appeared in *Theatre Arts* magazine, April 1955. I don't know of anybody else who has written about applause, although I'm sure many people have, especially psychiatrists.

Yesterday Hal X. phoned to ask if I'd write a play for him, in memory of the days when he was looking for work in New York and came to the rehearsals of Across the Board on Tomorrow Morning, ran errands and was generally helpful and amusing, without having a part in the play, or pay, or promise of a part.

"What does a world-famous movie star want with a play by me?" I said. "I write failures."

"Never mind the world-famous stuff," he said. "I want to spend a lot of time rehearsing and opening in a play that hasn't got a chance."

"I might just accidentally write a play that *has* got a chance."

"Have you got an idea for a play like that?"

"No."

"Well," Hal said, "I've got an idea for one that hasn't got a chance, and if you'll write it, I'll do it."

"What is the idea?"

"Applause," Hal said. "Do you know what I mean?"

"I've got an idea."

We talked a minute and I said I'd think about it. I remembered the applause Hitler created and came to count on, to enjoy and believe in. But what's the good of thinking about a man like that?

I considered next the applause of audiences at concerts. Why did certain conductors insist upon having a great deal of it, by various tricks? I then considered the applause given to political candidates, baseball players, actors and actresses in plays, in radio, on television.

What is applause? When it is valid, and when isn't it? Was there ever a first-rate man who was able to enjoy applause?

I thought of Darrow at the Mecca many years ago in New York, and his unmistakable annoyance at being applauded. The applause started and stopped almost at the same time. He just wanted no part of it, and the audience understood and respected his wish instantly. Had he been critical of the audience, or of himself? Neither, I think. He had been critical of emotionality. He was an intellectual, and a lonely one, and if he was to appear before a group of people, it was to be solely as himself, not as a creation of the audience. He didn't care for mobs, and the audience knew it. If they wanted him to maintain integrity and to respect each of them, they would have to put aside any herdlike rampaging. He had been nervous while he had waited for his turn. He had been miserable while someone had taken too long to introduce him. He had insisted upon no applause. He had spoken clearly, unemotionally, intelligently, quickly, and he had sat down. There was little applause at the end of his talk, but I doubt very much if this signified that he was not respected by the audience.

The next speaker, however, permitted applause, and at the end of his speech enjoyed something like an ovation. The same audience.

I consider the second man a fool, but in my thinking I employed the phrase which I find more accurate. I considered him a deliberate mischief-maker, a prolonger of herdish idiocies and hysteria, a fraud.

Is it ever in order for any man to accept applause from any group at all? In my opinion, it is not. And this immediately establishes a problem that deserves to be carefully considered—by others more systematic and more expert at this sort of thing than I am. The problem is this: If it is desirable for the human being to be both a sentient and an intelligent creature, how can he become such a creature if the herd habits which operate in his mass-life, which belittle his sentience and prevent his achievement of even the hope of intelligence, are permitted to persist?

To put it another way, if the most effective art is hysterical, if the achievement of its effectiveness is by means of emotionality, how can common life be serene, reflective, poised, intelligent?

I have heard, by way of a biographer and by way of a playwright, that Lincoln was bewildered by applause. Surely now and then, though, he must have been thankful for it. In short, he must have felt on occasion that he was entitled to it, for reasons he alone knew. They may have been excellent reasons, too. And he may not have been thinking at all about the reasons the applauders may have had to applaud him, or to seem to applaud him. For whom does anybody ever applaud but himself?

The church, which is so frequently inept in so many other things, begins and ends all of its performances without applause— with applause prohibited, in fact. My son once applauded at a rather hushed moment in a church in New York. The wave of astonishment and silence stopped him quickly.

In the street I asked him what had impelled him to clap his hands. "Well, when the man came out," he said, "didn't you *see* him?" I had indeed. Well, wasn't he dressed that way? Yes, he was. Perhaps. Then why was it wrong for him to applaud? And so on.

The fact is, applause does belong to children. The clapping of hands with joy is rather inevitable for them, as when my daughter was taken to the biggest and brightest department store during Christmas week in San Francisco. The minute she was beyond the revolving doors and inside the magnificent and enormous room, she clapped her hands and cried out, "Oh, Papa, look at that!" I had almost forgotten what a special and wonderful place it was, in fact, and how deserving of a large glance.

I shall never forget the producer of a play in New York at the end of a preview performance before an invited audience. He stood in the aisle, applauded wildly, and then began to stamp down the aisle toward the stage, shouting bravos and applauding as he went. The play had been far from flawless or meaningful. I had been the producer's guest. With what I felt was friendship, I said, "But you can't do that, can you?" The producer was deaf, however. But a producer—after all, what is a producer? What may one ever expect of a producer? Alas, he was a leading figure, if not the leading figure, in a kind of dynamic campaign to revitalize the American theatre. He was not a money-man, he was a man of high cultural aspirations. Had his applause been helpless? I doubt it, but if it had, all the worse. Had it been deliberate, almost part of the play itself, a kind of valid element in the potential wholeness and effectiveness of the play? Most likely, but again all the worse. You cannot in fact applaud (literally) that of which you yourself are part. You can for the fun of it, if you happen to be young and a little rambunctious, or even a little scornful of both the play and the audience. Other-

153

wise, you can't.

Now, it is easy to slide this whole subject over to an area of insignificance. Why, it might be said, we applaud solely because we are civil and polite. The whole business is nothing more than common civility. Applause does not need to be sincere, any more than saying good morning to a neighbor needs to be sincere. It is routine. There is no reason not to applaud, no reason not to greet a neighbor.

It is easy to say that applause, at its best, is a good and necessary thing, and it does not matter that most applause is for nothing and useless.

In reply to that I say it's noisy.

Will the good psychiatrist say applause is a safety valve? If he will, I will say, open the valve for sunrise and sunset, seashores, skies, mountains, meadows, rivers, lakes, forests, birds, insects, weeds, whatever. If disaster in drama impels or requires applause, why does disaster in the real world prohibit it?

But what is applause for a play? I presume it is intended to be thanks—to the playwright, to the players, to Heaven, to life, to art itself, if I may run a lot of things together quickly. Anonymous thanks, and what's wrong with that?

If the play is good, I suppose there's nothing wrong with it, although I don't like it on general principles.

But everything is applauded. A man on a television giveaway program is asked if he is married. He says he is. Applause. He says he isn't. Applause. He says he loves his wife and sounds as if he means it. Applause. He says he loves his wife and sounds as if he is only trying to get along with her. Applause. The next man on the program is a celebrated guest. He is one of the biggest men in the government. He signs the currency, for instance. He is asked if American currency is sound. He says it is. Applause. The following week on the same program, a dazzling, middle-aged woman with an accent is asked how she manages to be so pretty-looking all the time. She says, "Bot I vaz alvays very pretty—since leaddle goil." Applause.

What is this? In short, has applause—the device of it— nullified the hope of decent discrimination in all areas?

A girl has a round figure. A camera is turned on her. She is watched putting on a dress, pulling up her stockings, walking half a block. Applause. What for? Is it astonishing or miraculous that a girl has a round figure, knows how to put on a dress and is able to walk half a block? The movie ends and the newsreel comes on. The cabinet is in session before television cameras for the first time. A man says something that sounds as if it means something but doesn't, or certainly doesn't mean what the man implies it means. Applause. A captured bank robber walks to a train handcuffed to a plainclothes police officer. For a minute you don't know which is which. Then the smaller man turns and waves. Applause. The plainclothesman looks on shyly. After all, who is he?

What about the play for Hal X., fifteen short years ago a young man from a poor New York family looking for easy work (a part in a play), for the past ten years a name, face and figure known all over the world wherever American movies are shown?

Three years ago when we met by accident in New York, I said I was on my way to Pasha's on Allen Street because of the Near Eastern music and dancing there. Would he care to go along?

"Ah, they'll mob me," he said. "I haven't been able to go to places I like for years. I've got to go to 21, the Stork, Sardi's and all the rest of the places that are safe for celebrities."

I insisted that he wouldn't be mobbed at Pasha's. He was, however. The whole place was jammed with young Syrians, Greeks, Armenians, Turks, Jews, Spaniards and others in less than half an hour. We took a taxi back uptown and drank in peace, surrounded by other celebrities scared to death of the public, and its affection and applause.

He asked for it, though, didn't he?

Well, *did* he?

Hal X. is now thirty-six years old. He is not much unlike other men in their middle thirties. The mob at Pasha's included not one man who was not as interesting as Hal X. himself. The trouble with Hal is that he knows that. I don't think he especially dislikes what's happened to him. I can understand, however, that he might be a little fed-up with the unnecessary fuss that is made over him—for nothing. Now, if I could write a play about a man who doesn't enjoy applause, he feels sure he could go to work and really perform that part. No doubt, but it wouldn't help. He'd be applauded just the same. If the play failed, as it would, as he himself would prefer it to, he would be applauded, the good drama critics would only remark that he need not have wasted himself in such a part, and they would criticize the playwright for writing another bad play.

Still, the subject of applause deserves a play, no doubt. If I write it, Hal X. can have it, and good luck. He'll never have to put up with the public's affection and applause for the Vice-President, for instance, but at the same time he'll never again know the freedom and chance to grow in integrity that he knew when he was unknown and truly famous.

Homage to Baseball

Homage to Baseball was published in *Sports Illustrated* in October 1956, the last year of Ebbetts Field in Brooklyn.

Baseball is caring. Player and fan alike must care, or there is no game.

The caring is whole and constant, whether justified or hopeless, tender or angry, ribald or reverent. From the first pitch to the last out the caring continues. With a score of 6–0 in the bottom of the ninth, two outs, two strikes, nobody on, only an average batter at bat, it is still possible, and sometimes necessary, to believe something can still happen—for the simple reason that it *has* happened before, and very probably will again. And when it does, won't that be the day? Isn't that alone almost enough to live for, assuming there might just be little else? To witness so pure a demonstration of the unaccountable way by which the human spirit achieves stunning, unbelievable grandeur?

If the caring isn't for a team (because a team won't come through, or can't), then for the game itself, the annual ritual, moving with time and the world, the carefully planned and slowly accelerated approach to the great reward—the outcome, the answer, the revelation of the best, the winner.

It is good to care—in any dimension. More Americans put their spare (and purest?) caring into baseball than into anything else I can think of—and most of them put at least a little of it there. Most of them know the game is going on all the time, like the tides, and suspect there's a reason, or at least wonder about it. What is all the fuss about the whole year, and all the excitement every October? Is this a nation of kids, or what? Why not existentialism instead of baseball, for instance? Well, for one thing, you've got to be tired to care for existentialism, and Americans just aren't ready to be that tired yet. For another, baseball can be trusted, as great art can, and bad art can't, especially as it comes from Hollywood, where sharp dealing is an accepted principle of profit-making. And it doesn't matter that baseball is very, very big business —quite the contrary. That only makes its truth all the more touching and magnificent. It doesn't matter, either, that the great players don't think of baseball as I do, for instance. Why should they? It's enough for them to go after being great and then to be great—and then to be no longer able, as time goes by.

I'm devoted to the game, to all of the teams in both leagues and to the World Series, because I don't know of anything better of its kind to be devoted to—and it's always out there with that anonymous crowd of the hungry and faithful, watching and waiting, in the stadium—their eyes on the geometric design of the fresh diamond, all set for the unfolding of another episode in the great drama, which cannot be put anywhere else—not into movies, not onto the stage, not even onto the television screen (although that's pretty good when you're held captive somewhere 3,000 miles away from the great place and the grand moment), not into books, and not even into statistics, although the game has grown on statistics.

It's a game—the biggest and best and most decent yet. The idea is to win the most games in the American or the National League, and then to go on and win the World Series: to establish a statistic, and fix it forever to the ragtag experience of a whole people for a whole year.

I happen to be sorry Cincinnati didn't have the pitching, but they look awfully good for next year. It was great, too, the way Pittsburgh took off early in the season and then came back for a moment near the end and very nearly took the soul out of the Dodgers—but didn't, and that's the important thing as far as the Bums are concerned. I'm sorry, too, that Milwaukee got slugged by St. Louis, but you've got to like the Cardinals, too. You've got to like the game. No team is ever willing to stop caring. The fact is they can't, and there is the secret of the game's importance and appeal.

It is a tradition for the President to throw out the first ball of the season, but somewhere in the bleachers the poets are on hand, too.

157

I don't think you'd get Casey Stengel in any arena of human activity other than baseball, and not getting him would be a national disaster, unbeknownst as it might be. Alston, too—another kind entirely. Bragan, Tebbetts. All of them. Fighting it out with their players and their fans, their friends and enemies, umpires and newspapermen, but most of all facts and figures—statistics. You don't get Sandy Amoros, either, running in from left field as fast as he can go after an inning in which he dropped one he *had* caught —knowing it might cost the team the pennant. Knowing and waiting, and then hitting and saving the pennant, and then fielding and saving it, and then hitting and saving it again—knowing, saying nothing, on the theory (some say) that he doesn't speak much English. That could be it, all right, but there could be another theory, too, and the kids know it, and the old men and the old women know it, and the cab drivers and the cops and people in hospitals and penitentiaries and other lonely places. They don't know Sandy—but what he did, they know *that*. And it's a good thing to know. You wouldn't get Robinson, either—from the beginning. Or Williams, twice back from the wars, or the heroic return of Sal Maglie, and all the others, each made great and more deeply human than ever by the game.

Well, *is* it a game? Is that all it is? So the Dodgers win it again in 1956. So the Yanks win. So what? What good does that do the nation? What good does that do the world?

A little good. Quite a little.

And there's always next year, too.

The World Series of 1956, and the Perfect Game

The World Series of 1956, and the Perfect Game was written for *Sports Illustrated*.

The way we felt was, Let it go anyway it must, but let it be a good drama.

Let it do things other dramas, in other terms, by use of other devices, another order of language, another form of action, other involvements, in other arenas, street or office, store or factory, school or home, anywhere else, unmeasured and uncharted in terrain and time.

Let it speak of all things through the event, isolated, alone, but related in a hundred potential ways to a thousand potential progressions and to a whole end.

Let it create new heroes and new myths.

Let it move toward and then push past old and cherished limits.

Let the World Series be everybody's play, whether in four acts, five, six or seven.

And so it was—everybody's, and seven. Astonishing and seven. Unbelievable and seven. Magnificent and seven. Ridiculous and seven. One by one and seven.

At the beginning you stand and listen to the playing and singing of the National Anthem. The umpires and the players stand in the field and listen. There is something of the pride and humility of prayer in the pause and performance of the hymn. Whoever you are, on this field, in this stadium, the event that is about to begin is both yours alone, to value and measure and use as you will or must, and everybody's, if not in fact time's own, history's own. This event is abstract, impersonal and altogether for itself, but as it is engaged in by men from all over the nation, men not unlike anybody else, it is also personal and entirely for you—small boy with hot dog, and mustard on sleeve, priest with program and pencil, stenographer with aging father, bartender with small son and need of space and light and air and opportunity to shout, old widow with neighbor's daughter who knows what it's all about, professor of philosophy at Columbia, office worker with much work undone and buzzer ignored, the boys from the corner where the candy store is, the President, the Secretary of State, anybody, everybody. The singing is on behalf of the best of which human nature is capable or may one day be: physical to begin with, of course, since it is an athletic game, but of the spirit, too. A man's a man when he's abroad in the world, but on this field, in this game, he has been known to be more, to achieve instantly things known to be over the edge of his limits everywhere else, which for a fleeting moment carry him into a dimension of immortality. The hush of expectancy under the sky transforms the stadium into a cathedral.

After the anthem, you are entitled to watch and shout as you see fit. Now, when 30,000 or more at Ebbets Field watch and shout, it comes to a roar, happy or unhappy—for the achievement of one man is the frustration or failure of another. Some of the roar is for the achievement, some of it against the failure. If you don't take sides, you cheer because anybody has achieved, you groan because anybody has failed. This is a contest, a play, and all of the players together are yourself, and the play is about your life. If you must, you boo. You have a right to do that, however tactless it may be, or in bad taste. The booing can be therapeutic—sometimes to prod a child to sudden speedy growth at the age of 31. The crowd can be crude, rude, ill-tempered, offensive one minute, courteous and gallant the next, but it is never rude or courteous in relation to a player or a team entirely but in relation to itself, the crowd. And the identity of a crowd varies in accordance with what it witnesses.

A pitcher on the hill at the center of a small circle, a matador's ring, with an even tougher and more terrible opponent than a bull bred to believe in the unstoppable power of its eye and horn and brawn, with no such useful implement as cape or sword, with an even greater enemy—the next man's skill itself, his wit, his cunning, his control but, most dangerous of all, his unaccountable, unpredictable but always possible good luck. A man alone there facing another man alone, a man whose skill and wit and luck he knows and respects and fears but must cancel—now. It cannot be put off until he has had time to think a little more. The pitcher must face all of the hazards of throwing to his man, and then he must rear back and fire. He must deceive the enemy into swinging at something impossible to hit, or into hitting it in a manner that is harmless. Three times a pitcher must trick his man into not hitting in order to have him out, but if he goes too far four times he has only tricked himself, and the batter walks to first. Still, he must take his chance—strike him out, walk him, force him to hit harmlessly, or hear the crack and see the flight of a true hit, and watch, and wait. And start all over again.

As it is with the pitcher, so it is with the batter. The next event may be good, it may be bad. If it's good, it could be the game —the winning of it: a little event among the many that made the difference.

Nobody who saw the fifth game will forget the grand identity of the crowd at Yankee Stadium, nobody will forget the possibly religious anxiety, hopefulness and quietude of that crowd—a crowd created by the unseen but deeply felt presence in the stadium: the presence of the mortal spirit in proud and patient combat with flaw—error, wrong, spiritual pain, perhaps even death.

Something in the crowd took wing when Don Larsen pitched The Perfect Game. He did it. Of all the players, of all the people who might have done it, he did it. Nobody expected him to do it, but he went out there and started to pitch, and then little by little, inning by inning, he began to do it, and the very breathing of the crowd changed. Would he make it, or would somebody?—something?—himself?—anything? stop him cold? End it? Reduce it to just another game to put down on the books alongside thousands of others?

Would he do it?

He did.

There was no rudeness in the crowd. On the contrary, there was reverence—for man's life, for his small but sometimes great and immortal soul.

The Series had everything, or very nearly everything. First, it went the distance, and it certainly might not have—but saying that is nonsense. Nothing is swifter than time gone, or more final than fact established.

Sal Maglie pitched and won the first game for the Dodgers. He worked, as he always does, with intense concentration and control. The plate umpire examined the ball frequently for spit and tossed back a new ball, and Maglie pitched the new ball, and the same thing happened again, and he pitched it again and, if he spit, Casey Stengel himself said he couldn't say, and in any case his "fellas" (as he put it) didn't hit. It was a good game. It had form. Mickey Mantle homered early in the game, but it didn't stop Maglie. The form continued, and it was Maglie's. The Dodgers looked good behind him, and were. Jackie Robinson felt good nearby, and Roy Campanella catching, Pee Wee Reese, Jim Gilliam, Gil Hodges, Duke Snider and all the others. He was a kind of shepherd of the hill, so to say. He scowled and worked and didn't blow up when they hit his best stuff, and the players around him had to feel all right, and hit, and win, and they did.

A lot of things might have happened after the first game. A lot did, and there's no more guessing. What happened happened.

When Casey Stengel went out to the pitcher's mound four times during the second game, few were able not to feel that what he had had for so long wasn't working for him any more. Few were able not to feel that he might just lose this one, too, and then two more—and all of his great gains over the years. The Dodgers were hitting everything. They weren't letting him have his kind of game: a game with form. They were giving him a game in which past performances and percentages meant almost nothing. They were playing as if there had never been any such thing as statistics and all that had ever mattered in the game was high spirits, luck, enthusiasm, confidence, laughter, genius—give it any name you like. Who can take a game away from a team like that? What good are traditional tactics if they don't work? What good is knowing what you are doing and why, if nobody else knows? Or if they know something better and are doing it, perhaps for new reasons, perhaps better reasons, and everything is a shambles? How can the champions of the American League lose a six-run lead in one inning? What happened? Was it really all the consequence of a bobbled ball at first?

Two for the Dodgers, now, the big two, and two to go. Having started as they had, how could the Dodgers fail to take two more? How could the Yankees possibly take four out of five?

How? The way they did.

Whitey Ford came home to Yankee Stadium and pitched his team to their first win on Saturday, but it was still 2–1. And then on Sunday Tom Sturdivant went out there for Casey and did a good job and got into no real trouble until the ninth. Casey went out to the embattled hill to think with his pitcher and catcher, and Yogi

Berra told him Tom still had his stuff, so Casey let him stay in there and fight it out. And Tom Sturdivant went the distance and won his game. And so it was tied, 2–2.

Then came the game of the Series, the game of the year, the game of the past 30 or 35 years, the game everybody had been hoping for, not just this year or last, and not just for the Yanks but for any team, for any pitcher, and it was Don Larsen. Three for the Yanks, two for the Dodgers, but by now even their friends were beginning to call them The Bums again. But they hadn't done anything truly bad so far. Late in The Perfect Game Sandy Amoros had homered foul by a distance of half a foot. Duke Snider, slicing to left field, had sent one a little foul into the stands. The Yanks had done a lot of magnificent fielding behind Larsen. It was still anybody's Series.

You don't begrudge a win that comes out of a Perfect Game. Even Maglie, pitching a great game against Larsen, hoped in the last innings that Larsen would get it, and why not? There is a larger thing than winning, sometimes. It is sometimes nobler to lose a great achievement than to win against magnificence shattered, even by lucky accident. The Perfect Game was won by both pitchers, both teams, by baseball itself, but especially by the hushed and reverent crowd at Yankee Stadium. Everybody there was somebody named Don Larsen, and Don Larsen was just a little more than anybody else in the whole world, a little more than any man is permitted very often to be.

Now the play returned to Ebbets Field, Clem Labine for the Dodgers, Bob Turley for the Yanks, and they dueled at 0–0 through nine innings. If anything, the Yanks played better ball than the Dodgers. Turley pitched a game he was entitled to win, but didn't. In the 10th with two on, two outs, Jackie Robinson sent one out to Enos Slaughter who didn't touch it, that's all. Dodgers 1, Yanks, 0, the Series tied at 3–3.

Up to and including the sixth game the Series had enough variety, enough freedom and enough form for two or three Series (on account of The Perfect Game). One thing was lacking to give the Series everything: a game in which one team played out-and-out badly, in which it was inept, hypnotized, chloroformed, helpless, apathetic, sick, sorrowful, dead on its feet, tied in knots, twisted, tortured, confounded. And that team was the Dodgers in the seventh, 9–0. Young Johnny Kucks pitched low the whole game, and nobody could hit him. No excuses. No explanation. The Dodgers lost, and the next day took off by airplane for Japan, by way of the Hawaiian Islands.

What happened?

A baseball game happened. The poor part of it might have happened to the Yankees, but it happened to the Dodgers. Let the great psychiatrist try to explain how or why. There is art, for instance: great, ordinary and bad. But even bad art, even the worst, is better than no art at all, because the fact that here is such a thing at all is the important thing, and if it is almost always bad, at least now and then, once in a long while, it is great, and just a little of the great goes a long way. Forever, you might say. And in this Series there was quite a lot of art.

Baseball tells the nation's story. Among the reporters who regularly cover baseball are those who have become writers of style, wit and humor, and it may be that they are turning out the best folk writing of the nation.

Hong Kong

Hong Kong was written in Hong Kong on April 28, 1958, during a trip around the world. I wrote a piece a day during the voyage and mailed it to a small syndicate, which sold all of the pieces, except this one, which got lost. So here it is now.

Hong Kong is a British Crown Colony. On the map it is a pin-point on the southern edge of Red China, only 90 miles south of Canton, but in itself Hong Kong is a very big place, with a lot of people, around two and a half million, mainly Chinese, mainly poor.

An American dollar is worth almost six Hong Kong dollars.

Being a free port, certain things cost less in Hong Kong than anywhere else: clothes, cameras, watches, and so on.

There are scarcely ten thousand British in Hong Kong, but the place is biddy British. Biddy is the word for a kind of human style invented and maintained solely by the British. It consists of a passion for picayune authority, mumbled by great hulking career men with many initials after their names, who over the centuries made the empire, lost it, and might very well be feebleminded—by any standard of measurement so far devised. They seem to delight in doing the same dull and irrelevant things at the same time every day, year in and year out, with the same jolly excitement, the same inexhaustible capacity for not getting bored. Their war-cry is, *It can't be done,* but it scarcely occurs to them that what really can't be done is what they persist in believing *can:* to go right on being biddy British all over the world among enormous numbers of people who need a decent program by which to come alive. I admire and cherish the British at home, especially in London, but in Asia they are unbearable bores who accomplished a little on behalf of the people of Asia a hundred years ago, and then stopped for whiskey and soda.

The British had plenty of time to help the people of Asia to help themselves, but they either didn't know how, or they didn't want to.

They haven't, although they believe they have.

Their belief is unwarranted.

If the British and the United States don't know how to help Asia find a useful and hopeful program, or don't want Asia to have such a program, the people of Asia themselves will invent their own program, or go along with any other economic or cultural system that will help them. That would of course be Communism, a profane word in the English language to many people, but actually no more profane than the word Capitalism.

Russia is not a Communist state. It is a state theoretically committed to a faith in the ultimate superiority of Communist principles over Capitalist principles. They use the same devices used by England and the U.S., money loans, money gifts, trade, economic help, agricultural and technical assistance, but with this difference—a dynamic program to improve living for everybody. The fact that the program is partly theoretic doesn't diminish its appeal, for its purpose to help all of the people as quickly as possible is the only relevant purpose of our age. The competition England and the U.S. are getting from Russia is entirely on Capitalist terms, at which England and the U.S. are supposed to be experts, and it is this fact that may very well have to be identified as the grand coup of Stalin. Capitalism has no philosophy, that's all.

It is therefore touching to see the British trying to hang onto little edges of Asia as if Kipling were twenty years old and bright uniforms and highly polished boots on British soldiers were the means by which to measure the well-being of millions of people.

It's another time now. The British aren't equal to the challenge. They have proved that. The U.S. might be equal to it, but it will have to hurry.

The best cards are in the hands of the Russians, and they are playing them brilliantly. The image of a world card game may perhaps be apt, and even accurate, but it is silly and unfortunate, too.

The whole world and every human being in it is everybody's

business. The most powerful nations have simply got to go into business together, both on behalf of themselves, and on behalf of the great numbers of people whose agony, if neglected, may very well make humanity, not peace, impossible.

The U.S., England, Russia, and China have got to talk hard business.

This is not Communism. It is common sense. Biddy British or argumentative American isn't going to get it any more. We began to cook our own goose when we underrated the people who were far away and different. We can stop the cooking by noticing that the superior among them are superior to most of our own people, and that the inferior among them have just as good a potential for improvement as our own inferior.

National habits are hard to give up. The Russians are better at it than the Americans. They kicked out Communism soon after the revolution in favor of realism. It worked. It's working.

The job of inhabiting the world may simply be too much for the human race at its present stage of development, in which case we shall muddle through to something or other—which could be anything from simple stupor to final disaster.

Say I'm a Liar,
But I Love You.
Guess Who?

Say I'm a Liar, But I Love You. Guess Who? appeared in *Playboy* in 1964.

Breathes there a man with soul so dead that in his heart has never said, This is my own, my native land.

The foregoing is an incomplete and perhaps garbled version of a piece of fine writing I chanced upon almost fifty years ago at Emerson School in Fresno, and immediately loved for its simplicity, truth, and warmth; loved so deeply in fact that I found it impossible not to invent and declaim parodies of it, which nevertheless did not diminish my admiration for the original:

Breathes there a man with foot so flat that in his zigzag ramble from the watermelon patch has never said, This is my own, my stolen fruit, farmer, please don't shoot.

Or: Breathes there a man with mind so wrong that in his language class has never said, English is my own, my native tongue.

Or: Breathes there a man with heart so grim that in the summer has never said, This is my time to dive, and sink or swim.

The thing I liked about the piece of writing was the simple yet exalted arrangement of the first four words, *Breathes there a man,* which had the effect of making me feel, Now we're *talking.* And made me believe I could talk that way, too, and probably ought to, for the good of my own green but willing soul.

In ordinary everyday speech I had never heard anybody say

anything in that poetic manner, but now I knew it could be done, and therefore it was no longer necessary to imagine I would have to speak English as I had heard others speak it: I could speak it as others had *written* it.

I could speak *writing:* Dreams there a dreamer a dream more bright than my dream of you, Maxine, in the second-grade, two places forward, one aisle to the right?

The answer: No.

My dream of Maxine was actually impossible to talk about, let alone *write* about, but on Valentine's Day in 1916 when I was eight I tried to draw a picture about it: a heart with an arrow in it under the carefully printed name Maxine.

Below the heart was a whole great white space for my name, for *me,* for my life, my dream, my inexplicable and incommunicable adoration of this dumpy, stumpy, lumpy, lazy, light-headed, lisping little angel who had come directly from the spheres to enchant and torment me, although she lived in a kind of hovel on Santa Clara Avenue near O Street, the daughter of an Irish day-laborer.

There was space for my name as well as my message, but when I moved pencil-point, and eye and nose, secret and soul, to where I might begin to engrave the first letter of my name, I was stopped cold in my tracks.

I couldn't write my name.

I couldn't print the first initial of my first name, even, because in that great miracle, that great love, that great dream of Maxine, I was simply nothing—a total stranger, an outsider, an immigrant who actually wanted to invade a dimension in which he would be a crude clown, a rude fellow, an astonisher of the order and law, who would have to be laughed at and politely told to go back.

Who was I to think that I could send my drawing of love and adoration and my name and message to the Miracle of the Ages, Maxine Herself? How ridiculous and unfortunate each of my names was. How wrong, how hopeless.

I could talk a little *writing* all right, but I couldn't talk *love.* It was too big for language, line, sign, mark, engraving, letter, whisper, word, song, dance, glance, or thought: although for a while I expected thought to do what nothing else could. I believed my dumpy little darling would find arriving into her own mysterious thinking-and-feeling processes the *thought* of my love, and one day would suddenly turn, look at me, and be as glad about me as I was about her. She would get up from her desk, come to me, and I would get up and take her by the hand and walk out of the room with her, out of Emerson School, out of the Public School System of Fresno, and out of the whole foolishly complicated rigamarole of trying to get people to find out about love—we *knew* love, we *had* it, straight from the holy source of it, and so we didn't need to go to school any more.

We were ready to *live* only, because we knew love. A hundred years of the Public School System of Fresno and we would never learn anything better, so why should we hang around postponing everything, the ultimate and maximum? Why should we be the same as everybody else, who were unfortunately less lucky?

I thought my long deep thought of love, and waited for it to arrive in Maxine, so we could recognize one another and get out of there.

But after three full long January weeks of total failure, I began to suspect that the dream of love that had come unaccountably into my life *couldn't* be directed into the life of Maxine, and thereby make us truly wed one to the other.

I waited, and then I stopped waiting. *That* wedding wasn't happening.

Was it possible that it would never happen—all her life, all my life, all of everybody's life?

Was it possible that it simply *couldn't* happen? Couldn't we ever know something as simple as that *without* words? Couldn't we know it at just the right time because it was true—forever, beyond words, a truth which had always been and would always be?

Well, it looked as if we couldn't.

There simply was no communication between people apart from words, spoken or written, and so on Valentine's Day I began to make my Valentine for Maxine, only to discover that my love was so great, mysterious, everlasting, hopeless, crazy, true, and one-sided that I couldn't sign the Valentine, not even with my initials, not even with one of them, not even with the always-popular Guess Who?

And yet she was the one girl in the whole world for me, so what was a man to do about *that*?

Well, I would do something, most likely, something in writing, most likely, because if the substitute communication was language, then that would be the thing I would be concerned about the rest of my life. I would try to find out how to make the substitute communication that *is* in words as near to the real communication that is *not* in words.

I would find out how to send Valentines to Maxine—and to everybody else.

As for that particular Valentine on that particular Valentine's Day, I didn't send it. It was too inadequate a substitute for my love, and so I had to reject it entirely.

I received a few Valentines from girls I didn't like, I passed along a few to a few others I didn't dislike as much as I disliked the girls who had sent me Valentines, and I signed them Guess Who, or You Know Who.

The Valentines that came to me I shoved into the pocket of my overalls because they were not from Maxine, but every now and then the rest of that day, while I was selling papers, I brought them out and looked at them and put them back, and thought about them and about the girls who had drawn them and sent them, and then sure enough, little by little a kind of rather meaningful thing happened: I stopped disliking the girls. I rather *liked* them in fact. They weren't Maxine, I really didn't know *who* they were, but I rather liked them, substitutes as they were.

And I knew the Valentines didn't mean that they *liked* me, they meant something else, maybe something like, Well, here we are, stuck with ourselves, not in love with one another the way anybody knows love *really* is, but what do we care, it's still pretty wonderful to be who we are, anyhow.

And so I was glad that I had received three Valentines, and had sent four.

Love doesn't have to be perfect. Even imperfect, it is still the best thing there is, for the simple reason that it is the most common and constant truth of all, of *all* life, all law and order, the very thing which holds everything together, which permits everything to move along in time and be its wonderful or ordinary self—a rose is its own self, for instance, but no more its own self than a cabbage is its own self, although only a cabbage.

Breathes there a man with memory so feeble that on Valentine's Day his soul is not gladdened by sending to somebody a substitute message of his real love, or delighted by the arrival from somebody of the same substitute message?

As I am still breathing, I want to send a 1964 Valentine to the following:

1. My enemies, if I have any, which *they* know, and I don't: I love you. Opposition, animosity, rejection, even hatred made me, such as I am, which I am not prepared to belittle, and so my love, ladies and gentlemen, wherever you are.

2. The people I don't know, don't understand, and now and then tend to hate because they seem to be stupid, vicious, and determined to make the American version of the human experience

a monstrous thing: good luck in whatever the *real* fight is that you are fighting, which you probably don't even know you *are* fighting. If I can't love you, and I'm afraid you don't permit me to, I can't hate you, and I will not pity you. Only God can do that. (In case anybody is unable to decide who I'm talking about, and can't guess, try again next Valentine's Day.)

3. Red China—government, land, people, and all. You don't have to love me, but I've got to love you, because you're beautiful, and sooner or later even Marxism can be seen to be as earnestly imperfect but hopeful and human as Jeffersonism. We shall learn from one another, and not only live and let live, but *help* live, and not hinder, you us or us you.

The rest of my Valentines are purely personal: everybody I have ever known and now and then perhaps hurt; everybody whose kindnesses to me I haven't cherished, my daughter, my son, my dead father, my dead mother, *all* of my dead: we don't get along, we don't understand one another, we talk too much, we say too little, we hardly ever make sense, and almost never the simple sense of simple love, but I love you.

Say I'm a liar and that *this* is a lie. I still say I love you. Guess Who?

A New Idea in the World

A New Idea in the World was written at the invitation of the editors of *Look* magazine, and published in the first issue for the year 1957.

An idea is coming to pass in our time. It is so simple as to seem oversimple and therefore complex, and it might be considered revolutionary. It isn't quite an achievement, discovery, truth or condition. It hasn't been defined, identified or named. And yet it has the makings of something likely to save man's soul.

It seems to have begun in the past 20 years.

In 20 years, a boy born in New York and a girl born in San Francisco can learn to walk and talk; read and write; sing, dance, play the piano or the violin; work in an office, on a farm, in a shop or a factory; take sick or be injured; become healed or mended; travel; meet as strangers; fall in love; quarrel, separate, make up; marry and become the parents of a son or a daughter.

Their 20 years have had natural form and personal meaning, because, from the beginning, the passing time has coincided with their physical growth and their intellectual development.

To one degree or another, the remaining years of their lives will continue to have this sort of personal meaning—this sort of promise of physical and intellectual fulfillment. But never again will time be quite so alive, so intense or so charged with the mysterious and the wonderful.

Fate has been at work. The human will has been at work. A

great deal of human expectancy has been fulfilled by the birth of a child. To most of us, this seems to be very nearly the greatest fulfillment and the greatest achievement of all. In a sense, it is.

In the 20-odd centuries since ancient Greece, Shakespeare did his work and died. Mozart did his. So did Socrates, Jesus, Galileo, Columbus, Newton, El Greco, Voltaire, St. Francis and millions of others, named and unnamed.

In our own times, in the past 20 years, Gandhi did his work. Einstein did his. So did Whitehead, Saarinen, Toscanini, Santayana, Brancusi, O'Neill, Sibelius, Dreiser, Chaplin, Nijinsky, Shaw, Schweitzer, and many others.

In his own time, what should a man do? What can he do? If it's easy to do, is it worth doing? If it's not easy, is it worth the trouble? Why should Tensing and Hillary climb the highest mountain? Why should Roger Bannister run a mile in under four minutes? Why should Picasso paint so many things so many ways? And why should so many people at the United Nations, from so many places with so many different ways of thinking and living, work so patiently trying to understand one another? The sun comes up and the sun goes down anyway, doesn't it? Man is an animal, isn't he? Why should he go to so much trouble about the kind of animal he is? What's he trying to prove? Who's he trying to impress?

Children grow and have children, and someone on television with a touch of genius makes them laugh. What's Jackie Gleason do that for? Is the need to laugh the consequence of always being so close to sorrow—about insignificance, unimportance, uselessness, inability, ineffectuality, anxiety, fear, regret, guilt? But what did man do, or fail to do, to put him so near sorrow in the first place?

In human time, the latest year is always the most interesting, the most difficult, dangerous, promising and wonderful. During 1956, Grace Kelly married Prince Rainier III of Monaco, the South made a painful try at integration, and Russian tanks pushed back the Hungarian people in the streets of Budapest.

In 1937, the names were different, but again the year was interesting, difficult, dangerous, promising and wonderful. England's Edward VIII abdicated and married America's Wally Simpson; the Dust Bowl farmers set out for California; Hitler strutted on the stage of Europe; and the State of Eire was born. In these 20 years, as in the 20-odd centuries, ideas happened.

Ideas always happen. Sometimes it seems as if they happen to only a few of the human beings in the world, and then sometimes it seems as if they happen to all of them.

The ideas are always about birth and death, reality and illusion, right and wrong, truth and falsehood, love and hate, acquisition and loss, or all of these things together—as well as others.

A great deal can always be said and done about ideas one way or another; and one way or another a great deal *is* said and done about them all the time, by all kinds of people, for all kinds of reasons.

Large numbers of people have always lined up on one side in opposition to large or small numbers on another side, about ideas. Very seldom has anybody clearly understood anybody else. It frequently follows, therefore, that somebody must be overcome, imprisoned, driven out, or killed. And it is always easy to find law and language by which to justify all such acts. Most of the time, the acts are hysterical, sometimes they are monstrous and criminal, but as they are also official, they are always considered righteous, intelligent, necessary and useful.

The theory is that the majority has got to be right. Some of the time this is a good theory. It is never, however, a better theory than the theory that the individual is as likely to be right as the group, for the reason that every member of a group is also an individual, and for the further reason that a hundred frightened or unhappy individuals in a group are not likely to be nearer truth and right than one frightened or unhappy individual not in a group.

Large numbers of individuals are impressive in terms of arithmetic only, as one million is more than one, for instance. If a subtler or more worthy impressiveness is to be achieved, it must be achieved in other terms—weight-lifting, high-diving, corn-husking, butterfly-catching, stamp-collecting, money-making, child-bearing, poetry-writing, picture-painting, symphony-composing.

If the nature and truth of man were to be measured by numbers, man might soon find ants worthy of deification, and after ants (in a higher form of religion), microbes, and then atoms or electrons, since there are so many more of these things than there are of men.

But man is measured by his ideas, and the great ones continue to be few and far between.

Many people seem to suspect that the emergence of the idea of the last twenty years, 1937–1957, is near. Some *like* the idea, some are grateful for it, some are afraid of it, some are bewildered by it.

The idea wasn't tried for. It came to pass as a result of something else that was tried for, and achieved.

What *is* the idea?

It is many things, all of them the consequence of the fact that

175

it is now impossible to do unto others as you would *not* have them do unto you—on account of the enormity of the thing tried for and achieved: nuclear fission and fusion.

In 1939, a genius wrote a letter to the President of the United States saying that, because $E = MC^2$, an explosive could be built bigger and more powerful than anything man had ever dreamed of. The President ordered the work to begin, and scientists began their experiments. They made one crucial test in a football stadium in Chicago in 1942, and another in New Mexico in July 1945, and then in August a B-29 crew under orders carried the experiment to Japan.

Since Hiroshima and Nagasaki, the explosive has grown greater and greater, but so has the idea.

Now, it comes to something like this:

Whoever you are, you are also the other, whoever he is; and whatever you do to him, you do also to yourself. So do you want to do it? If it's something death-dealing, you don't want to, unless you're mad. And that is why the idea began.

Physical force has always been the means by which one large group has imposed its will and way on another large group, or on an assortment of small groups. But that may not work any more.

Consequently, a new means by which to resolve difficult problems and basic differences among peoples must be discovered and put to use.

That is the idea in its simplest terms.

There are certain easy ways by which to seek to prevent the idea from flourishing. One way is to limit the amount of force employed. The trouble with this scheme is that the other fellow has got to "promise" to limit the retaliated amount of force, but suppose he doesn't? Since the big war ended, there have been a number of little limited wars and the unspoken promise—we won't use our bomb if you don't use yours—hasn't been broken. But that doesn't mean it can't be broken, or won't be.

This compels pause and thought, which in turn compels a fresh examination of some of the words we live by: right, truth, justice, victory.

How can you win, if there is no longer any such thing as winning, in terms of force and numbers? If physical force is no longer a usable power, except upon time and matter, and not upon man himself, then the idea must be to discover and to exercise other forms of usable power—moral, intellectual, spiritual, and cultural.

With the old habit of force and the old theory of winning nullified, what can you do, except try for something better? You try, not by choice, but by necessity, because what you tried for and achieved was just a little too much, at first, to keep secret (remember the day Harry Truman announced that the U.S.S.R. had exploded its bomb?), then a little too much to use (remember the news stories about what an H-bomb could do to New York?), then a little too much to fret about forever (what happened to civil defense?).

Already, the idea has compelled a lot of slowing-down, even while things have been made to move faster. But the faster things move, the slower anger or arrogance may be *permitted* to move.

Unformed and unresolved as it is, the potentialities of the idea are great, and good. Its ever-unfolding fulfillment appears to be unavoidable.

But then, man can be foolishly clever, and the idea may be frustrated and thrust aside for another 20 years, another century, or even forever.

On the other hand, it may begin to be truly fulfilled during 1957, a new year and therefore again the most interesting, the most difficult, dangerous and most promising of all.

American Acting

American Acting came out in Cue magazine, in March 1956.

Whenever I see Actors Studio actors in movies or in plays I find it impossible not to curse. Russia, that is—as I believe it's safe to do that, as it would be at the funeral of a thief to praise Texas.

But Russia is a large order, and inasmuch as our bitterest enemies become our warmest friends in a generation, perhaps it would be wiser to curse a Russian. Stanislavsky, for instance, even though I never knew him and don't really have anything against him. He appears to have taught acting, pretty much instead of going to church or to a psychiatrist.

And then he died, and people far away took up teaching acting, too.

The scheme is to teach people to be comfortable imitating somebody. It is very complicated and boring, except to the girls and women and the hysterical men who want to become famous and rich imitating people in plays—the students, so to call them. Many of them, as I understand the matter, are famous and rich, but this does not deliver the situation from any of its basic fatuousness.

There are very famous people in America who might just as well not be famous, that's all.

All art has probably always attracted incompetents, but probably no art, excepting perhaps painting, has rewarded the stubborn incompetent so handsomely as the art of the theatre. Virtually no talent of any kind at all is required other than a kind of idiot determination—but this does not mean that the art of the theatre is not an important art, or that many theatre people are not real artists with real greatness.

It only means that you, too—as the ads go—whoever you are, may both drink Coca-Cola and be in the theatre. Do you want to be in the theatre? Why shouldn't you be in the theatre? Plays are about people, and you're one of them, aren't you? And so on. If you don't want to act, you can direct. If you don't want to direct, you can produce. If you don't want to produce, you can teach. If you don't want to teach, you can study, but not so much for the purpose of going on the stage as for—well, why not study? It's nice. It's conversational. There's endless talk connected with it. And isn't endlessness and talk what everybody really wants most of all? Of course it is.

Excepting The Iceman Cometh, the very best theatre in America bores me—and a lot of it over the past ten years has been very skillful, very effective, very clever. It bores me because of its subject matter, its purpose (or rather lack of it), its hysteria, and its general and profound phoniness. The Iceman Cometh is a sick play, by a playwright apparently sick to death, but it is the sombre and tragic sickness of a great soul—not O'Neill's soul, but the soul of the human race.

As for the films of the past ten years, they bore me even more than the plays do.

Plays.

Movies.

What next? Operas?

O.K., operas. I don't like them. I consider the American ones I've heard—some of them again and again, annually, so to say— spurious. I haven't heard many foreign new ones, if in fact I've heard any at all. I don't like them, either.

The time has come—as if there was ever a time that was inappropriate for it— for intelligence to temper all art. For art to leave both the kindergarten and the looneybin.

I think we might gather, then, that I don't like any of the art going on at all. Perhaps I don't.

I can find little fault with nature, and I expect art to reveal the meaning, beauty, truth, and humor of nature—on behalf of the growth in grace of man himself—now.

Hysteria, however grand or touching or effective, ain't going to get it, as the saying is. Theatrical—and that includes operatic— effectiveness appears to have gotten itself bogged down in overemotionality, and that ain't going to get it, either. Not any more. We've done that, and done it very well, too, and enough's enough.

What Do We Want Art to Do?

What Do We Want Art to Do? appeared in *The Nation* in April 1955.

I have been thinking for some time about theatrical art in general and the art of the musical comedy in particular. What are they? What ought they to be?

The end result of my thinking is that I consider a "system" or "philosophy" of theatrical art useless, although it can give the untalented a momentary feeling of security. (Security on the stage, in their work? No, just in themselves, at home, or in the street.)

This brings up the whole matter of theatrical systems and techniques, which to this day are being followed from longer than fifty years ago. In fact, the most skilled players have been schooled in one or another of the old systems.

Anything wrong with the systems?

Yes. A system may very well make an order of effectiveness inevitable, but it is here that the mischief begins. The order may very well be undesirable, as I think the order of most current theatrical and film effectiveness is undesirable—in that it is unimaginative, repetitious, and in a deep sense both meaningless and destructive.

Let us take, for instance, the film that is supposed to be the best of the earnest films of last year, On the Waterfront. This is a bad film, and yet it gives an impression of being good. Effectiveness is achieved, but it is an artificial, not artful, effectiveness in that the fable pretends to be real, or even super-real—done right on the waterfront itself, for instance. The result is that there is neither fable nor truth, even though all performances may be considered skilled, and one or two touched by greatness, or comparative superiority. But what is the film saying, in any language? It is saying the names of those who are connected with it. The unanimity of the "voting" in favor of the film has some sort of meaning, I suppose, but not much. Now, even Chaplin's effectiveness has grown unsatisfactory with time, but if you want to get a relative idea about what such a fable might have been, just impose Chaplin's system or technique on the story: the purposeless "heaviness" of everything is supplanted by speed and wit: the almost embarrassing emotionality is thrust aside by an order of *sentiment* which is still pretty much universal, if by now useless.

Or to get closer to the form of the musical, let us take The Saint of Bleecker Street, also unanimously acclaimed, and also bad, both in choice and in use of material. What is *this* work saying? For all its involvement in various things, it is saying the name of the composer—which is the point that now needs to be made.

All of Shakespeare says Shakespeare with an effectiveness which has become intrenched, but which may not necessarily be the end of the life of effectiveness—or to put it another way, the only order of effectiveness of the plays.

What is the precise order of Shakespeare's effectiveness? Out of basic passions and preoccupations—out of elemental plots in the tragedies, and tricky plots in the comedies, and fairly narrative plots in the histories—come first an order of usage of English which remains irresistible in spite of the fact that it is overloaded with vast amounts of word-jingling for its own sake, and second a satisfying, or fairly satisfying, order of resolution, or conclusiveness.

Hamlet is mad. Hamlet demonstrates how being mad is not entirely just that, how it is almost always also being brilliant, wise, gentle, vicious, gallant, amusing, stupid, and all the other things any great man who is mad might very well be. Hamlet lays about him wildly and eloquently and foolishly, drives others mad, kills them, is killed, and ends by again saying Shakespeare, or the writer who can do anything—a little better or a little more unaccountably than anybody else. The name Shakespeare is the name of his humanity and genius, or his view of the world and time, and human life on and in them. But is Shakespeare's dramatic effectiveness the ultimate of the potential of effectiveness? It is not. Whose is? Nobody's, at the moment, but then Shakespeare's rivals haven't worked very well or very hard.

181

What do we want art to do? What is it for? Until we consider these questions, we are apt to be carried away by the useless and repetitious in art. We want art to impel human life toward the achievement of its best potential, which is to thrive, in all of the implications and dimensions of that condition. To thrive with love, zest, and humor, and to endure pain and the meaninglessness of life and death with grace and humility. In short, to be, if not great, at least a little less small than a creature with intellect and memory ought to be.

Excitement is the device—or "gimmick," to use a currently popular term—of drama, and this is the source of the mischief. But is it possible to convey the tragic nature of human life without the use of excitement? It isn't easy, but it is possible, and the challenge of doing so, or of trying to do so, is becoming greater every day with our awareness of the absurdity of the logical carrying-through of the principle of excitement in the time of nuclear realities. If the effectiveness of art is to continue to reside in human excitement, how can the destructive use of such nuclear realities be avoided? And if art achieves effectiveness in calm and in intelligence, how can the nuclear realities not reject their relationship to weaponry? If the human soul is an idiot's, and human brilliance and power are a maniac's, how can the human race get to heaven, so to put it? The nuclear weapon, in a sense, was used against the human race in Shakespeare's finest tragedies. The contemporary dramatist, or artist of any kind, has the responsibility of transforming weapon into worker—in everything he creates. The collective intelligence of the nuclear men has to be matched by the collective humanity (love) of the fable men—the writers and artists. To report chaos and hate is not to put order into chaos or to banish hate. The potentials for order and love are inherent in human life and just as easy to achieve as their opposites—and certainly a lot more practical, if nothing else.

How do you do it? You do it by trying to do it, and failing, most likely, and then trying again. One of Joyce's basic principles has gone a little too unnoticed, I think: that he would not permit himself to use material that might achieve effectiveness because it happened to be violent. Was this a criticism of most of Shakespeare's work? A rejection of almost all dramatic, and much literary, effectiveness? Yes, that would seem so. If you're going to have murder and madness in art, then you're going to have them in life, too.

But isn't it the other way around? Murder and madness in life, and therefore also in art. Yes, that is the theory all right, but somebody goofed there. It doesn't matter that real men and women go mad, and that they kill one another. With compassion for them, they just don't happen to be the means by which to measure or by which to improve the nature of the survivors—and art and everything else is always concerned with the survivors. The dead, whoever they are, cease to be anybody's concern the minute they are dead.

What is the purpose of a musical, since I began a moment ago by being concerned about that? It is the same as the purpose of all art—to impel or encourage the human being to thrive pleasantly, intelligently, with dignity, without fear or hate, and with humor and grace. That's quite a lot to try to do with a jazz band and dancing girls, but it can be done.

The Hoax of Success

The Hoax of Success was written sometime during the middle 1950s, and appears here for the first time.

One of the rich young women of America was credited in the newspapers and over television and radio not long ago with a remark that went something like this:

"Wealth stinks. I wish I were poor."

One news commentator scoffed at the woman's sincerity—the one I happened to hear. I don't know about the others. In all probability they scoffed, too. The popular attitude appears to be: "It's easy for somebody with five or ten million dollars, and an annual income of another million, to belittle wealth."

This attitude fails to recognize the real significance of the remark, however. If the experience of living has little grace and less meaning, the possession of great wealth doesn't improve matters. Loss of fortune, or even forfeiture of it, would not of course bring grace and meaning into the individual's experience, but the desperation of the remark deserves at least respectful notice.

The woman *is* poor, as a matter of fact. What she is saying is she wishes she were rich.

The wealth she longs for is not measured in number of dollars stashed in vaults, records, and archives. It is an order of wealth not easy to come by—for the rich or for the poor.

As a matter of fact, a paraphrase of the remark might have

been made by anybody in the U.S. who has inherited or earned wealth or success, either, or both. Privately, something of the sort *is* said every day by every successful American, excepting idiots, thieves, psychopaths, and phonies, to whom the possession of six pairs of shoes, for instance, constitutes adequate glory, honor, and immortality for all practical purposes. It isn't necessary to begrudge such people their pleasure. They are the last of the Americans not to recognize that they have been taken in by the national hoax of success. They may very well run the nation the rest of the way downhill to smash and trash.

I can't be concerned about wealth in money, but I am concerned about success, or more properly the illusion of it in the U.S.

At the outset it is necessary to understand that it is possible for *anybody* to be "successful" in business, in the arts, in entertainment, in (even) religion. The only thing required is the desire, supported by stubbornness and energy. Success *will* come.

There are new "successes" every year in every field of activity. They all succeed, they all earn unbelievably large sums of money, they all appear in the newspapers, in the magazines, on television. And then their admirers, their fans, settle down and very nearly say to one another, "So what? It doesn't help." New racehorses come along every year, too, and their success is not unlike the success of the new men and women. Trainers train them, jockeys get on them, they race, they win, they lose, and they are retired. The arrival and departure of the horses mean a little something, because the horses are bred for racing. With the men and women it's not so simple.

Let's say a man with a little real character does a little real work. This is so astonishing to everybody that he is rewarded immediately with money, and offers of more money. If he has had little money most of his life (and most people have had little), it is understandable that he will be pleased to have a lot for a change. He will soon even learn the ropes—how to work in a way that will bring more and more money, how to be surrounded by people who can get the best results from what he does, and how to arrange matters so that almost none of his money will go to the Tax Collector. Soon the man with a little talent is a big business. He thinks differently, sees differently, works differently. The small amount of talent he started with doesn't grow. It doesn't have a chance to grow. It stands still, and marks time, and then it moves backwards, and finally the little is gone. In its place is a fair sum of money, and some sort of fame or notoriety.

Why are Americans obsessed by a longing for obvious (and spurious) success? That is, money and publicity? Obviously because they are hungry, because they aren't very much in themselves, one by one, and must become "real" or interesting or talented by means of a bogus fable created by publicity agents; gossip columnists; newspaper, magazine, radio and television reporters and interviewers. Why will they do very nearly anything free of charge that will feed this insatiable hunger? Again obviously, because they are frightened, even terrified, that it won't last: and of course it won't, it can't, the fable just isn't supported by anything enduring, anything that can be made to endure, anything authentic.

No area of activity is exempt from this national aspiration for money and attention at any cost—priests, taxi-drivers, druggists, heiresses, labor leaders, agents, criminals, automobile manufacturers, detectives, corporation lawyers, tax-evasion experts, window-washers.

Judges and Chiefs of Police gather together to ask each other on television why there is so much juvenile delinquency, as it's called, and why it is increasing everywhere. Nobody is willing to suggest that a large part of American youth is just plain stupid; and that they are encouraged in this unnatural condition by adults, including television playwrights who achieve hysterical drama by demonstrating that a fifteen-year-old moist-eyed sniveling monster runs with a gang that beats old women because the poor little fellow's mother didn't embrace him every morning before he went to school, or his brilliant father didn't share his interest in hot rods, rock 'n' roll, and marijuana.

The nation isn't cracking up necessarily, but it is awfully sick from spuriousness, and from a lack of men of integrity, recognized and respected for it.

The kids are only chasing their own version of the same spurious fame and importance. They are only doing in their own way with their own limitations what they have been encouraged to do by the examples set by the celebrated adults. They are only younger nonentities seeking to pass for fabled characters—boys who don't chicken, girls who don't quit when the going gets crazy because they don't expect to marry and settle down and be wives and mothers some day anyway, so what's the difference?—they expect to win beauty contests, become models, actresses, and international characters.

The little unfortunates were reared not by their miserable mothers and fathers but by N.B.C., C.B.S., A.B.C., comic strips, tabloid papers, movies, songwriters, and a whole culture that is pitiful, while it takes pride in claiming to be free, true, liberal, wise, and the greatest culture of all time.

Well, material wealth with nothing to go with it stinks.

For the people who have no wealth, who are poor not because they have very little money but because they have very little identity, very little character, very little resources, poverty stinks, too.

If this nation is going to survive meaningfully, and then perhaps to grow decently, it has got to begin to know and accept enormous deprivation. A twenty-year moratorium on all substitutes for honor would at least be a beginning.

Tijuana the Tramp Town
of Lower California

Tijuana the Tramp Town of Lower California appeared in *Rogue* magazine in 1962.

Tiajuana or Tijuana as it is both pronounced and spelled might be said to mean Aunt Juana or Aunti Johna, who is certainly nothing like anybody's aunt from Peoria. Tijuana is so near Hot Water, or Agua Caliente, they are virtually the same town, or certainly parts of the same general idea, which at its best is a good idea and at its worst not a bad one.

The city lies just barely across the United States border in lower California or Mexico, but it is not quite possible to believe it is an authentic Mexican city; it is less than twenty miles south of the heart of San Diego which is the jumping-off point of thousands of daily American visitors, but Tijuana cannot be considered an American city, either. It is too far from Mexico City to be Mexican and too near Army, Navy, and Marine installations to be considered American. Essentially it has no real relationship to either nation, although it is by turns cherished, tolerated, regretted, despised, and finally defended by both. Tijuana's permanent residents eagerly welcome the tourists with money in their pockets, although it is impossible not to notice an occasional gleam of contempt in the eye of the native as his souvenirs, entertainments, or services moves the money from the tourist's to the native's pocket. But it isn't a sincere contempt, it is amiable, and sometimes even affectionate. Many visitors know enough Mexican to pretend they are not tourists, and almost all natives speak passable English, so that language is almost never the source of any misunderstanding or the cause of any disputes or fights, of which the town has surprisingly few. The native only wants to make as much money as possible from the visitor, who in turn only wants to get full value for his crisp green and his hard silver. This kind of understanding tends to reduce the causes of disputes to the usual basic two: temporary stupidity due to alcohol, or an unaccountable personality aberration. Gang fights or riots are virtually unknown. Nobody from the U.S. seems impelled to look down on the Mexicans, who over the years have acquired the patience and cheeriness of members of American service clubs.

Going to a foreign country for many people is the setting free of a hungry, thirsty, emotion-starved, noble prisoner who must become as quickly as possible the large generous hero he has cruelly been prevented from being for so long—by custom, convention, fear of exposure, gossip, neighbors, family, tattletales and fuddy-duddies. Id, ego and unnamed or unnamable submerged forces leap out of the prisoner's chemistry, quicken his pulse, deepen his voice, strengthen his muscles, and send him roaring to where the action is. Town idlers and hustlers loafing around on the Tijuana side of the border gate can spot such visitors in a glance, even when the visitors are not in uniform, even when they are not high-spirited kids from sober homes in the Midwest, the East, the South, the North, or the Far West. *Any* boy in uniform is considered to be *always* ready to eat, drink, gamble, and be merry; but he hardly ever has much more than a few dollars to spend. A hustler, or guide, prefers a male adult out of uniform, because he knows that soon Operation Freedom, Fun, and Folly may be launched, at a pretty good profit to all, including the guide.

There is nothing fancy about the fancy houses of Tijuana. Strictly speaking they cannot be considered houses at all in the traditional sense, although there are better than two-dozen places whose girls are stamped medically O.K. These girls are generally young (but never underage), neither elegant nor expert, as the girls and women in traditional houses would be, and not, contrary to what one might imagine, predominantly Mexican. As a matter of fact American girls predominate, and they are generally dope addicts, runaways from pimps, ex-convicts, social misfits, women who are mentally retarded, and a handful of physically ordinary or even ugly but intellectually brilliant women who have fallen into Tijuana prostitution out of boredom, for thrills, for a stake (on which to return to husbands and children frequently, and now and then to university classes), or in order to avoid hospitalization for a break-down. The advantages of working in Tijuana are attractive: most of the clients are kids who pay anywhere from two to six dollars and use up only as many minutes. The girls can work as little or as long as they choose, take up with a favorite at a private place free of charge or for a large sum of money, are not the slaves of the underworld, and feel they are living their usual lives, rather than doing unfortunate work.

Many social experts believe that prostitution is quite simply unavoidable, and has ever been so, although in the Communist world it has *almost* disappeared; but at no time since the revolution has it ever been *totally* eradicated, and recently there has been a resurgence which may indicate the essential similarity of life on both sides of the Iron Curtain. The spy-sexpot of Communist countries is not strictly speaking a prostitute at all. She is a working girl whose master is not a pimp in the syndicate but an agent of the secret police.

In Tijuana prostitution is only part of the overall program to keep the city attractive to money-spenders. Everybody in the local government remarks politely if privately that there would be no prostitution at all if the tourists did not insist on it. The tourists are mainly Americans, the patrons of the houses are mainly members of the armed forces. "We do not mind rendering this service which San Diego is not permitted by public opinion to render. We consider ourselves only a suburb of San Diego."

Tijuana's biggest attraction, however, is its location, its reputation, its difference, its raffishness, and finally its dirt. Comparatively speaking, the town is small. The permanent population of Tijuana is 11,000, of Agua Caliente 9,000. Tijuana is drab and dismal. None of its people could possibly be considered smart, stylish, or chic. Only the heart of the town has paved streets. The smell of dust and dirt is everywhere. Dogs without collars, owners, or friends roam about incessantly.

I can remember no American town in which there has been this doggy quality in the streets, and in the total identity of the town itself.

Tijuana is also a hot town. Shade trees are rare, and grubby. Bird life is pretty much what one would be compelled to expect in such a setting: dry little unsinging birds scavenge in the gutters, and lazy hawks and buzzards hover over the rooftops.

A great many visitors to Tijuana go there only to stroll through the streets, look into the shops, and have a photograph taken by one of the many street photographers who furnish donkeys, carts,

190

and sombreros free of charge. These are people who enjoy towns as towns.

Most visitors, however, want to get as much as possible out of Tijuana that they can't get where they live.

One of the most popular of these things and perhaps the most truly Mexican is the bullfights Sunday afternoons. The bullring itself is unknown anywhere in the United States. The bullfighters have been and still are some of the greatest in the world, including Carlos Arruzo who now breeds fighting bulls near Tijuana. The regular spectators include many Americans, generally from Hollywood, whose veteran is Gilbert Roland, a Mexican by birth and the proud son of a matador. At one time or another, however, very nearly every actor and actress in the movies has gone to the Tijuana bullfights and joined the townspeople in being moved by angry animal and brave man in a ballet struggle between brute force and fragile skill, gradually blending into majestic harmony. The drive from Hollywood to Tijuana covers a distance of 120 miles requiring about three hours. Many working people make the round trip on the day of the fights, morning to night, making a big memorable day of high excitement.

Another truly Mexican attraction is the cockfight, but its appeal to Americans is very limited. A visitor to one of the three or four better cockpits in town will find himself in a very small arena that has a peculiar smell: a smell perhaps of anxiety, fear, tension, brutality, stupidity, avarice, frustration, and six or seven other variations of living-deathliness. The gamblers are desperate men who avoid violence by witnessing the violence of the demented little birds. The visitor will find few if any other Americans in the dismal arena, even though breeders of fighting cocks are in action in every state of the union, and it isn't likely that there is any state in the union in which illegal cockfights are not regularly staged. The betting in Tijuana is petty, although breeders and owners frequently bet heavily in private, especially Americans, especially Texans, many of whom breed very nearly the gamest fighting cocks in the world. The Mexican tends to bet Mexican breeders and birds, even when a Texas owner is known for his consistently superior fighters. I have tried to understand this. It seems to be plain ordinary Mexicanism, so to put it. The Mexican seems to feel that it is himself in the fight, and so of course it would be inconceivable that he would be willing to bet on his opponent.

The cockfights of Tijuana may actually be a sporting event of some kind, but the element of sport is almost totally concealed by

191

a great body of racial, cultural, geographic, economic, and aesthetic complications. The tension in the cockpit is unlike the tension at any other sporting event; it is picayune, nerve-wracking, interior, and nitwit, while the tension at the bullfights, for instance, is large, open and to many a tragic ennoblement of the whole human spirit.

As a native of California, of the great San Joaquin Valley, of the city of Fresno, I began to hear about Tijuana when I was a kid, and I began to visit the town in the late nineteen twenties, at which time the town had a magnificent gambling casino. I shot craps, played blackjack, and now and then flipped a silver dollar onto a number on the roulette table. There was also chuck-a-luck, large spinning wheels, lotteries, stud and lowball. Somewhere along the line the casino was outlawed, but other forms of gambling were permitted.

At the great Jai Alai Palace, there are bars, restaurants, reserved and unreserved seats, and pari-mutuel betting. The Agua Caliente race track has both pari-mutuel and licensed track bookie betting. There is also dog racing every night. Thus, even though there is no casino, anybody with money burning a hole in his britches can get action at the horse and dog races, jai alai, and cockfights.

There is still no way to gamble on the bullfights.

An almost dry riverbed marks the line dividing Mexico from the United States at Tijuana. Alongside this riverbed are a variety of shanties and shacks in which people make their homes, parents rear their children, and children love their mangy dogs, but the poor people of Tijuana are much less poor than the poor people of other places in Mexico. This is so because of the nearness of Tijuana to America and America's money, more than twenty million dollars of which is spent every year by five million visitors—on admissions, food, drink, souvenirs, leather goods, pottery, carved silver, coarse rugs, fine drapes, shawls, hotels, gambling, and nightclubs.

Tijuana's main street, Pancho Villa, is not more than three hundred yards from the border gate, so that the visitor virtually steps directly into a foreign world. The street has six blocks, both sides of which are crowded with saloon-cabarets in which guitarists, singers, dancers, comics, and strippers work steadily from early in the afternoon to early the following morning, or as long as there is somebody on hand with money to spend. The street also has hotels, restaurants, and stores. Most visitors like to take an exploratory promenade to the Jai Alai Palace and back on the opposite side: after which, they are ready to decide where to go and what to do.

The saloon-cabarets attract the most people, and certainly the liveliest. Between seven and eleven at night these places are crowded with noisy, excited, happy people, most of them under thirty, male, and in uniform. But there are always plenty of girls around, both Mexican and American, and after a performer has worked on the small stage and gotten back into her regular clothes she returns to the bar or to a table, to talk and drink and eat and laugh and argue with her new friends. Mexican beer is world-famous for its superior quality, even among experienced beer-drinkers, and so it is by far the most popular drink in town. In a cabaret a bottle of beer costs a dollar, but there is nothing else to pay in order to stay and see the show. The average visitor to a cabaret stays an hour and has two bottles of beer, although no one embarrasses anybody who chooses to have one bottle and to stay longer than an hour. The food at the cabarets is mainly American, although Mexican food is available if anybody insists. Few do. The quality of the food varies from good to excellent, but for diners who are intent upon dining rather than upon having a high and hearty time there are other and better places to obtain both Mexican and American food, one of which is the dining room of the Cesar Hotel. The quality of the entertainment also varies, but this time the range is greater, from downright lousy to absolutely inspired. The overall average of Tijuana talent would have to be given a rating first of special, then satisfying, and finally unforgettable, both for excellence and its opposite. There are always several first-rate guitar-and-song trios, who invariably somewhere in a song crow like roosters or squeal like pigs or simply cheer wildly like little children in the presence of glory. A soprano sings sorrowful love songs. And now and then a clown makes laughter, speaking both Mexican and English. Outside each of the cabarets is a barker in a crazy red uniform who quickly falls into a confidential whisper about the goings-on inside.

The tourist traffic is sixty percent young men in uniform; thirty percent men and women who visit the city more than six or seven times a year and generally spend a weekend; ten percent travelers from all over the country and from all over the world.

Anybody who spends a night in Tijuana will be unable to forget the concerto of noises which do not stop until morning: laughter, fragments of Mexican and American songs, shouted names, loud talk, pistol shots, footsteps, running, racing motors, horns, braking shrieks, and the banging of car doors.

There is a lot of free entertainment in watching the buying-and-selling on Pancho Villa Street: well-dressed young men and young women stand in the doorways of shops and speak to the promenaders about the treasures that may be obtained inside for very little money. The promenaders in turn smile and pass by or stop to chat and finally to enter the shop. Leather goods are of excellent quality and low in price. My son and daughter on a visit in 1958 noticed the form and progress of many price-disputes, which almost always were won by the buyer, so that at last my son said, "Let's buy something, so we can argue a little, too."

We went into a store and selected a leather handbag my daughter believed would cost thirty dollars in Beverly Hills. The young man who showed us the bag said, "This is the best bag we make. In San Francisco it would cost forty dollars, but our price is only twenty."

"Twenty dollars?" my daughter gasped. "Oh, no, that's much too much."

Excellent, my son's glance said. He nodded that I was next.

"Is there something special about the leather? Is it from an unusual animal?"

"From a horse," the young man said.

"Leather from a horse?" my son said. "Why should a bag made out of leather from a horse cost twenty dollars? I know a boy in Pacific Palisades whose father bought him a *whole* horse for twenty dollars. And it was alive. He *rode* it."

"Fifteen dollars, then," the young man said.

My turn: "I don't think so."

"How much will you pay?"

"Well, I don't know. I'd like to pay a *fair* price of course, my daughter likes the bag, but I don't think it's up to *me* to name the price, I can only let you know how much I *can't* pay."

"Twelve dollars?"

No answer.

"Ten?"

Silence.

"Six?"

Still, no answer.

"All right, give me five dollars and take it."

"I don't know," my daughter said. "I really don't think I like it, after all."

"This beautiful bag?" the young man said. "It's the best. *Of course* you like it. Four dollars, then—but please don't tell anybody.

"Why?" my son said.

"Four dollars is too little for this bag."

194

"Why should we pay four dollars if we can't tell anybody about it?" my son said.

"If we pay *three*," my daughter said, "can we tell one or two carefully selected people—in the family?"

At last the salesman smiled, and then broke into loud laughter, waving that he understood our game.

"Three dollars," he said. "Tell everybody."

Before leaving the store we also bought a hand-carved belt for my son without any dispute at all, and a plain belt for myself.

Tijuana is a kind of scalawag's Disneyland. In three years I took my kids once to Disneyland and three times to Tijuana.

One Sunday at the bullfights a young Mexican leaped into the ring after a bad bull had refused to fight and had created an outrageous situation. The bull was standing stock still and snorting, lassoed around the neck, the horns, and one front foot, and held fast by three cowboys. The young man from the stands ran directly to the bull before anybody could stop him. The bull lunged forward, hooked the boy through the stomach, tossed him high, and after the boy had fallen, began to hook him again and again. The hapless lad tried to get up, tried to get away, failed, and finally stopped moving at all. Like everybody else the three of us watched in loud and angry disbelief, and then my daughter began to weep because nobody was able to stop the bull and help the boy. We occupied a private enclosed box just beyond the ring wall, and so I turned them both away from the unfortunate scene, saying, "This sort of thing doesn't happen very often, but it did happen just now, and you saw it, and I'm sorry, but perhaps it's just as well."

The boy was carried away at last, a loose lump over a cowboy's shoulder. If he wasn't dead, he would soon be. The disgraceful bull was removed from the ring, order was restored, and after a fanfare a new bull came raging into the ring, and the bullfights continued. My son and daughter returned to their places, to watch. On our way home to Malibu that night my daughter said, "He died, didn't he?"

"Well, we don't know. People are tough, especially poor people, especially Mexicans. Maybe he didn't."

She certainly never had seen anything like that at Disneyland, or anywhere else. It was something to *avoid* seeing, if possible, but having by accident seen it, having been shocked by the swift folly of the boy, the sudden flaring of rage in the bull, and the failure of the boy to protect himself by any means, who can say what deeper compassion for both the human race and the race of animals may have entered her soul?

Tijuana is a tramp town, free, unkempt, scornful of convention, both disreputable and dignified, both trivial and tragic, but above all things unabashedly itself.

It is changing all the time of course, and with the explosive growth of California, it is almost inevitable that Tijuana shall soon become another kind of city entirely: a resort city, a holiday town, a rich, orderly, handsome place, with a prosperous permanent population and a continuous ebb and flow of people on holiday. When that happens other towns just across the California border will come into being, and these new towns will be as Tijuana had been for so long: a good dirty unimportant town for good solid citizens to lose themselves in for a while, for the good of their souls.

A Walk in New York

A Walk in New York was written in New York in the Fall of 1948 and appears here for the first time.

The immortality of cities is insignificant in eternity, but in the world cities hang on longer than any man is able to, so that there are times during long walks in the streets of a great city when the walker feels he is walking with the dead, or rather with the death-less, for aren't the streets always full of people?

The walker feels he is walking through the timeless world itself, made of light and night, labor and dream, fulfillment and failure, secret and riddle. It were as if he were immortal *now*, and time had no better truth.

To walk anywhere is both a simple pleasure and a rare privi-lege, but a walk in New York constitutes for me a kind of inexplica-ble if unimportant achievement of personal immortality.

To begin with, New York was where the European stepped off the boat, where my father did in 1905, and all the other immigrants from the highlands of Armenia. They had lived in Bitlis far back in time, beyond memory, but now they were in New York. When-ever they met in the streets the word was a look, rather than any-thing spoken. The Bowery was where they found their first Ameri-can rooms, and there that they walked with the immigrants from Spain, Italy, Serbia, Greece, Roumania, Bulgaria, Poland, Lithuania, and all of the other places of Europe.

They were kids, most of them, when they reached New York. They found work and sent money home so that other members of a family might make the long voyage away from home, too. A man and his wife and kids were reunited in New York after a separation of a year or two, and then they considered where to settle for good. Many stayed in New York as if the first place were the best, too. But others went up to the industrial cities of New England, to Pittsburgh, Detroit, Chicago, and to the cities of the Far West. But wherever they went, New York was always in their memories. They never stopped talking about it.

In California I heard the talk, and there was never any doubt in my mind where I wanted to go: where the immigrants first walked in America.

I finally reached New York from California in 1928, a few days before I was twenty. At last I saw the streets my father saw in 1905 when he was thirty-one.

At the New York Hotel, not far from the Bowery, I took a room for which the rent was three dollars a week. Nearby was the famous Woolworth Building, the wholesale produce district, the Hudson River, and the docks.

At the Public Library on Fifth Avenue I examined the Directory for the address of the widow of the man after whom I had been named, and one afternoon, after work at the Postal Telegraph office on Warren Street in the produce district, I knocked at the door of a house on a quiet street in Brooklyn. The door was opened by a handsome woman of sixty or seventy who said very quietly, "You are Armenak Saroyan's son. Please come in."

She told me about my father's life in New York, and she mentioned The Church of All Nations, where my father had been employed as a janitor, and where he gave a number of sermons in English. She also mentioned that he had written for *The Christian Herald,* and had been her husband's assistant in his work of finding rooms and employment for newly-arrived immigrants.

The following day I found The Church of All Nations in the Bowery and spent some time there. I could not feel anything but respect and affection for the little church and for the man who had befriended my father and thousands of other immigrants: William Stonehill, D.D.

To this day any time I am in New York I walk to the Bowery, aware that my father walked there fifty years ago, and that I first walked there almost thirty years ago, and that my son and daughter walked with me there last year.

A walk in the city should have no time limit, but that doesn't mean the walker might not choose to walk swiftly. The fact is that after the first half hour I pick up a rather swift pace which is maintained until I reach a place I must notice particularly.

A walk may have style no less than a work of writing. A lucky walk can be unforgettable, as if it were a first-rate story, play, piece of music, or a series of paintings, drawings, lithographs, or photographs.

There are few walkers who, at one time or another during a long city walk, do not get near one order or another of dream-like experience—as when suddenly the walker comes face to face with somebody he hadn't seen in years, and only an instant earlier knew he would. He will feel that this accidental meeting happened precisely this way before. But where? Was it in sleep? If so, sleep of long ago, or sleep of an instant ago, while he walked? (Is sleep continuous in a man from the time he draws his first breath to the time he breathes his last?)

On my walks in the Bowery I like to step into one or another of the bars for a glass of draft beer for a dime and the company of the drinkers there, and I have never felt that I have been slumming. I have felt as much at home as I have felt anywhere else, and I have found the conversation of the drinkers as true and reasonable as the talk of drinkers in other places.

To walk at all is to be alive. To walk in New York is to be immortal with the world and the deathless-dead.

What young ghosts of great men the walker greets as he goes: Washington, Franklin, Lincoln, Poe, Stephen Foster, O. Henry, Walt Whitman, Jack Johnson, Caruso, Knut Hamsun, George Bellows, Sousa, Ty Cobb, J. P. Morgan, Gorky, William Jennings Bryan, Eugene O'Neill, Christy Mathewson, John Barrymore, Billy Sunday, Theodore Dreiser, George Gershwin, Babe Ruth.

What proud times and places the walker reaches one by one, each with its own indestructible family and lore: Carnegie, Mecca, Palace, Metropolitan, Greenwich, the Bowery, the Battery.

Best of all, what earnest and mirthful light and truth the walker sees and hears in the faces and voices of the children of the world at play in the streets: Little Annie Rooney and her Joe, Mamie O'Rourke, Rose of Washington Square, the kids of song and fable still alive and still in tender love with time, world, and promise.

What sweet sorrow and shy dignity the walker sees in the eyes of lonely old men and old women at their park games, or gathered together under park trees to chat of yesterday, and perhaps tomorrow.

What eagerness and hope he notices in the eyes of the new immigrants.

What smells of cheese and bread and wine and garlic from the Italian grocer's, of roast pork and duck and tea from the Chinese restaurant. Pizza, sukiyaki, paella, hamburgers, hot dogs.

What scents of fresh-caught fish, roasting coffee, baking bread, oranges from Florida, apples from Oregon, grapes from California, figs and raisins and dates and dried peaches and apricots.

What life in the air to breathe, the whole world still alive and still hungry, because a man is still on his feet, and able to walk.

Losses

Losses appeared in *The Reporter* in November 1954.

I have been reading around in Maxim Gorky's *Reminiscences of Tolstoy*. I had read around in the book several times before, over a period of seven or eight years. The first time I read the book I knew I would be reading it again. I do not believe I have read it straight through yet, and I think I know why. I don't want writing like that to end. I only want it to be there. Night before last, for instance, I read the Introduction by Mark Van Doren for the first time. For me writing like that is better without beginning or end. It is beautiful writing. There is no other word by which to describe it.

My reading of Gorky has evoked memories of all kinds, including the broken promise of the Russians in Moscow in 1935 to allow me to go with the Armenian poet Charentz to see Gorky—because I had written my impressions of Soviet Russia truthfully, which offended them. That was a great loss to me.

In 1900 Chekhov urges Gorky in a letter to go to India. Gorky says he does not want to go to India. Why should he? Chekhov tells him that it will not take long to go to India and come back, and then forever after he will have India to remember. On sleepless nights it will be a great comfort.

I knew (when Charentz told me that Gorky was receiving writers of every nationality in the Soviet Union) that I wanted to see Gorky, too. I hadn't read his writing straight through. I wasn't a Gorky expert. I didn't in fact especially like his novels, but I had read some of his short stories and *The Lower Depths* and some of his *Childhood*. I wanted to see Gorky. Charentz said I would. The Russians of Moscow asked me to write my impressions. I wrote them. Charentz told me I had been prohibited from visiting Gorky on account of what I had written. I argued with the Russians of Moscow for two hours, but in the end I did not see Gorky, and he died, and I have never seen him.

The memory of that loss—and I consider it a great one, a very great one indeed, although I only meant to look at him from a distance, to watch him move, to listen to him speak—the memory of that loss brought memories of other losses, and I have gotten up out of bed to sit down and write them.

The death of my father before I was three was not a loss because I did not know about death at all, but I put it down first, as if it were the first loss, even though it was not a loss of any kind at all until a number of years later when I began to understand death.

I did not lose pride when I broke down and wept because my mother had left me in the waiting room adjoining the office of the orphanage in Oakland to which I was taken several months later, but I put this down second because it happened, and it constituted a loss of pride, whether I knew it or not.

My mother worked as a housemaid in San Francisco and out of her earnings sent me an inexpensive pair of blue coveralls that I was proud of—because they were a gift from my mother. I outgrew them and saw them one day on a smaller boy, and he had wet his pants. I became angry at him both for wearing the coveralls and for wetting them, and I complained about this to the Superintendent of the orphanage. I put this third because it constituted the loss of something. Understanding, love, charity, compassion. The Superintendent rebuked me, and I hated him for it, and lost nothing by hating him, for I had a right to hate him, and a reason to do so, even though he was right. But I was four and he was forty-four.

These are odds and ends of losses, I suppose. I have, as a matter of fact, been thinking about another order of losses entirely. It is just that losses are losses, and thinking about one kind puts you to thinking about all kinds, or any kind. For instance, I lost a lot of dignity when I began to go to public schools. That is to say, the teachers belittled me because I was not a comfortable person to have in a class. I was restless and bored and showed it, and the teachers resented this.

Somewhere along the line I lost faith, too—faith in people, in their integrity, in their honesty, in their goodness. I lost faith in other things, too. For instance, I had always loved America, for it was the only place I knew, but when my belief that I was an American was corrected by adults occupying important positions I lost faith in America, too. I was an American of course, they said—but just a moment. Wasn't I an Armenian? Yes, of course. Silence, and the memory that in Fresno an Armenian is an outcast.

In thinking about losses (even as I continued to read Gorky) I also thought about how I have balanced them. I suppose the loss of my father was balanced when I became my own father, as I did, I suppose; and when I rejected the church-God father but accepted God as my father; and when I thought of writers like Dickens and Maupassant as my father.

One day I lost a badge that had cost me that very day one dollar. It was a badge worn by the boys of Fresno who sold *The Fresno Evening Herald.* I never found that badge, although I looked all over town for it. Vahan Minasian, my mother's sister's husband, balanced that loss for me. He said, "Sahgh m'nah koo jan." Literally, "Long live your soul." Or, "A loss like that is nothing. It is not a loss in the soul."

In my youth I thought I lost a lot of valuable time, but I may have been mistaken. I was always eager to get full value out of time, so to put it, and this eagerness probably made me feel that I was losing time, that I had lost time. During the flu epidemic that killed so many people in Fresno when I was a small boy I came down with the sickness too, but I don't remember having felt that I lost time while I was ill. I remember trying very hard to understand illness and death, for they are variations of the same thing— but not simple things at all, and very difficult to talk about. When I was only eleven or twelve I lost a tooth. I have never balanced that terrible loss. The only thing I gained from that loss was the wisdom that I—I myself—was a thing in which mysterious decay could take place against my will or wish, a very vulnerable thing, a thing perishing even while it was not yet fully formed, like an unripe apple with a small worm in it.

I lost no money at all, as money is lost when it falls through a hole in the pocket or is stolen, but I gambled with money and lost quite a bit of it. Very often, more often than not, whenever I gambled I lost all the money I had. I balanced such losses by not gambling for a while and by working very hard, especially after I had become a writer. The reason I wrote The Human Comedy in eleven days, for instance, was that I had gone to Las Vegas and in one night had lost three thousand dollars, which at that time was a lot of money. Before I was broke, though, I made fifty-dollar bets at crap tables for men who were broke at three o'clock in the morning, and I won many of those bets, and handed many of those men fifty silver dollars. I was showing my contempt for money, and for what it did to men. I was showing off, too. I stopped showing off, or at any rate slowed down, the three years I was in the Army. I didn't stop entirely, but it wasn't the same thing at all. If I had lost the need or wish or ability to show off, I would have lost a very valuable thing, I think, and I can't imagine how I would be able to balance that loss, although I do not for a minute believe it cannot be balanced. It probably can, and probably should.

Every time I bought real estate, I lost. I balanced those losses as I balanced losses at gambling, by extra work. I bought a house on a hill overlooking a river in Fresno a few years after I got out of the Army, because I had first seen the place as a small boy at a picnic. The real-estate man said the place was a steal. He said the whole forty acres of barren land was composed of something he called puma tile, an ashy soil out of which bricks are made for the building of homes. He said the brick-makers would do all the work and pay me so much a ton. He said I could always get my money back any time I wanted to. But when I moved to New York six months later and wanted my money back, I got less than five thousand for the seventeen thousand five hundred I had paid. The Internal Revenue didn't allow the loss as a deduction, either.

But what is a loss? Is there in fact any such thing? Gorky (who put me to thinking of losses) died one year after I was prohibited from seeing him. He lost his life, as the saying is. He speaks in 1900 of his two-year-old son, whom he refers to as a charlatan shouting at his mother to leave the room immediately. Was the loss of Gorky's life balanced by that boy, now fifty-six years old, if in fact he himself has not lost his life, or his mind, or something else entirely canceling? We do not hear of anybody known as Maxim Gorky's son.

Gorky hated Tolstoy, and Tolstoy knew it, and they loved one another in a way that is altogether understandable. Gorky hated Tolstoy's need to spread his "religion," which was a silly one as far as Gorky was concerned, but he kept noticing that Tolstoy himself, apart from his foot-kissing cultists, was a man with a great and true soul, the only man Gorky had ever met who was God-like. Is this open mixing of hate and love a kind of Russian thing that should be looked into? Gorky was a kind of national hero and shrine of the young Soviet Union. Did he find the Russians of his last years different from the Russians of his early ones? I wonder. Is it impossible to deal with the Russians, as popular opinion seems to believe? I suppose it is if popular opinion says so, but there is also the chance that popular opinion ought to read a little of Gorky and then decide for itself.

What is to be lost from thinking as well of the Russians as we tend to think of ourselves, for instance? Or from thinking as little of ourselves as we are able to think of the Russians or anybody else? I can see no possibility of any loss at all. But if I am mistaken, and there *can* be a loss, and if the loss is apt to be a loss of money— well, that's another thing. A money loss you can always balance by a little extra work. And when you discover you can do a little extra work, you have discovered that you are not yet seriously sick, and not yet too old for the game, and that is a good discovery for a young man or an old man, a young nation or an old nation.

Sons and Fathers

Sons and Fathers appeared in *The Reporter* in October 1956.

One night in New York in 1941 there was an old man who said he decided early in his life not to father any children because he didn't feel he had the right to impose himself on anybody else. He didn't want to see himself continuing in anybody else. He was about sixty, and he appeared to be still mad at his father, and not especially pleased about his mother, either. He was a friend of a drama critic I had been drinking with, so he sat at our table.

I hadn't found a wife at that time. If I had any kids, I didn't know about them, which of course is the same as not having any. But what the man said was silly and a lie. He had an inferiority complex, although that in itself is not necessarily an undesirable thing, for I've never known anybody who didn't have some kind of a feeling of inferiority in relation to somebody or something. At the same time he was bragging. He was a man of wealth and of a certain order of achievement in a mixture of chemistry and electronics. He seemed to be well up on everything going on in pretty much all of the new fields of scientific research, experimentation, and discovery. He had come from nothing, from a big family of nobodies, as he put it, and he had turned out to be the only one of the lot who had gotten anywhere at all. He dressed properly, for instance, and carried a stick.

The critic had been telling me about the kind of girl he was looking for, and he had gone on a little after the arrival of the richer and older man, and that was how the richer man had come to talk about having decided never to be a father. He seemed to be saying that when they made him, they broke the mold. It seemed entirely unnecessary for him to say that, however, for the fact is they hadn't broken the mold at all. There were a great many others out of the same mold, and there would always be.

As it happened, the drama critic never found the girl he believed he was looking for, although he found a good many others. Well, just what sort of a girl had he been looking for? A perfect girl, of course, and he probably knew he'd never find her, although I couldn't at the time see why not. If he couldn't find her, he could create her. And if he couldn't do that, he could compromise like everybody else.

The rich man's theory astonished me, though, for I couldn't imagine any man not having as the primary purpose of his life the finding of a wife, the making of a home, and the beholding of his own children. I couldn't see how anything else could possibly be more basic and primary in any man's life, but little by little as the years went by I noticed that there were many men who didn't have that primary purpose and as a matter of fact were opposed to it.

I remember when I first read Liliom by Ferenc Molnar how impressed and moved I was by the simplicity and clarity of that purpose in the play.

Molnar himself came to New York and was sitting in Sardi's one night when I was introduced to him. Now, things happen, foolish and strange and yet somehow meaningful, too. When I heard his name I said, "But Molnar's dead." This didn't offend him, although it embarrassed me. There was another Mid-European playwright whose stuff I had read in *Vanity Fair* and in books, and *he* had died, and I had gotten the two names mixed up. I couldn't think of the other playwright's name, and while I was trying to think of it, in order to announce it and somewhat diminish the folly of my remark, Molnar said first that he felt flattered to have been thought of as being dead, and then he said the fact was that in a very real sense he *was* dead.

This all happened in high spirits, but I didn't like having said what I had said, and I wanted to remember the name of the other playwright but couldn't. When you're trying to remember something and at the same time trying to listen to what others are saying and to reply to what they are saying, this searching for the forgotten thing makes almost anything you say seem a little strange, a little disconnected, and possibly even witty. There were five or six of us at the table, which became noisy with laughter after everything I said. I just couldn't remember the other writer's name. A week or two later it came to me, and I was astonished that it should ever have been confused with Molnar's: Arthur Schnitzler. I ran into somebody who had been at the table at Sardi's that night and I told him to please tell Molnar I had been thinking of Schnitzler, and the following night Molnar asked me and the man to have dinner with him. And so from time to time I saw him, and each time I saw him he was gentler than the time before, more deeply hushed and more resigned to the sorrow that seemed to have seized him, that seemed to have come from a profound loss. Was it the death of the woman in whom much of himself had had its truest reality? His banishment from his native land, and from his beloved Budapest? The end of a whole world of which he had been both an important and pleasant part?

New York was fine, but he was never able to make the scene. It was full of Hungarians, but they were just as lost as he was, although a number of them were too busy to notice. After the war I saw him again from time to time, but by then the loss appeared to be total, and there was no push in him to return to Budapest. It was all over. Budapest was another place and another thing entirely now.

Late in 1948 when I saw him several times I began to feel some of the same sort of loss in my own life, and he noticed this. He said that as a young man he had gone to his father about a profound loss in his life: the woman he had loved had thrown him over for somebody else. Molnar had believed that the only solution to the problem was suicide. His father had said that that might very well be so, but first to start the writing of a new play and not to stop until it was finished. And then if he still felt that suicide was the only solution, that would be the proper time for it. Molnar said that he heeded the words of his father and immediately went to work. He worked hard and steadily, and soon the play was finished. The name of it was Liliom. Everybody at dinner was amused and one of the women said, "And so again a woman has been the cause of the making of a work of art." Molnar smiled, and the woman's husband said, "And of course after writing the play the woman meant nothing to you." Again Molnar smiled, but this time he spoke, too. "No, I could *still* commit suicide over that woman. But now I can't sit down and write that way any more, for *any* reason."

And then there was an American playwright, only a little older than myself and only a few years on the scene before me. One wintry day early in 1949 when we met unexpectedly in the street he said, "Let's sit down somewhere and have a drink and talk." Well, I didn't expect the drink to be tea, but that's what it was. He was speaking of himself, of course: "Everything that happens to you, however painful, you must use as a writer, you must be grateful for, you must add to everything else you have and know."

Well, I was in a bad way by that time, and this news made me laugh, for I had come to the same conclusion as a small boy. And I had lived by it. Now, though, I wasn't finding it so easy to live by any longer, because it was no longer myself alone, it was also my son and my daughter, and their mother. I was divided into a number of parts, and that which had been valid for me undivided just wasn't valid for me any longer. I was in the others, but without the control of them that I had always had of myself. The most important parts of me were here and there, where I couldn't get at them and hold them together, and this was all new to me.

Something lingers in the human family that is from certain branches of the animal family. Total love, straight through to issue, to children, can be a killer, and no man who is killed by love is ever again the same, or ever again a son. He is a father forever after.

I Don't Get It

I Don't Get It appeared in *Playboy* in 1966.

I have a jealous nature, so I don't have any trouble at all hating a great many people every day, especially when I am reminded that they are being mistakenly considered greater than I am, when they get too successful, too rich, too important, too big for their britches. I see photographs of them on the covers of magazines or on the inside pages, or in newspapers, and dozens of long paragraphs about them, and I flip. What the devil's the matter with this country? Here I am, the greatest, and these second raters, these counterfeiters, these phonies, grab all of the attention, and sometimes all of the girls, too.

Now it's Arthur Miller, now Edward Albee, now Arthur Kopit, Jack Kerouac, Jack Gelber, Paddy Chayefsky, where did all these guys come from? And these aren't the only ones who make the wig flip: What about Allen Ginsberg, Gregory Corso, Lawrence Ferlinghetti and a lot of other guys writing poetry and making a lot of noise? And then there are the geniuses of the movie business— what was that guy's name who always talked fast and made at least five thousand dollars a week every week of his life—every time I think of him, even without being able to remember his name, just remembering his jumping personality, I feel this country is nuts, this culture we've got isn't a real culture. And then there are the geniuses of television—not the actors, the hell with the actors, everybody makes allowances for actors, it's part of their good luck for actors to be unconscious, and the more they try to acquire intelligence, the more hopeless the situation becomes like that poor bastard who was born feebleminded but nevertheless worked hard at acting and finally got a fairly good part, about a strong simple man, or at any rate that's how it came across in the movie—well, this poor man began to go on television in all kinds of interviews, and he worked at being so humble that anybody could see he actually believed he was *that* big, that it was permissible for him to be humble, and it wasn't, he was only entitled to be arrogant and stupid, by birth, by nature, just as by birth and by nature I am jealous and suspicious—of everybody who gets noticed more than I do, and for 30 years almost nobody in the whole country has been noticed less.

I hate these kids. They gripe me. Give me men like D. H. Lawrence, H. G. Wells, H. L. Mencken and H. Rider Haggard—dead. Such men, such superior men, I like, I love, I cherish. They don't go hogging all the attention, all the magazine and newspaper space, all the money, all the fun. And what about Henry Miller—an older man, entirely without a lovable nickname, no palsy-walsy side to him at all, but still a grabber—*Tropic* of this, *Tropic* of that, he knew some sloppy girls, that's all, so everybody says he's surely one of the great writers of our time, and nobody says anything about me. That's not right.

I don't begrudge Alexander Pope his fame, he's entitled to it, but these other kids, where do they keep coming from, most of them irreligious, too, many of them blasphemous, several unbathing. I respect William Blake his fame—he worked hard for it, and honestly. Besides, while he was alive he must have felt a little like I have always felt—lousy, because William Blake wasn't considered the great man during his lifetime that he was. I think Bill Blake is entitled to every bit of his belated fame, and the thing that burns me up about Bill is that he didn't get rich, all kinds of other people got rich, but Bill didn't, he started poor and he stayed poor his whole life. And I'll be damned if I want that sort of thing to happen to me, too, having the same first name, but so far not having encouraged a lovable nickname. I could long ago have encouraged everybody to call me Bill. In fact, long ago I was called *Wild* Bill ten or eleven times by newspaper reviewers of books, but I soon enough noticed that they called anybody whose first name was William the same lovable Wild Bill, and God knows *all* of us Williams weren't wild or certainly not equally wild. The reviewers weren't sincere, and one thing a suspicious man is everlastingly concerned about is the sincerity of his admirers. Are they sincere, the nonentities? I am an entity. I have been an entity all of my life. It hurts an entity to find all kinds of nonentities, or only recently graduated entities, getting all of the attention.

It isn't easy for me to be comfortable about never having been on the cover of *Time,* for instance. What does *Time* mean by bypassing me year after year? Do they mean to imply that these other kids who are getting on the cover are more important than I am? I'll be damned if they are. I'll be damned if anybody who has ever been on the cover of *Time* is more important than I am. I happen to understand about importance. I'm an expert at it. I know who is important and who isn't. And towering over and above everything I know is the proud and lonely fact that I am the most important of all, so what's *Time* trying to do, confuse me? Well, brother, just remember one thing. I can get hot, but I'm awfully difficult to confuse.

Nobody, but nobody, is going to tell me I'm not the most. I am. I was the most when everybody else was struggling bitterly to become a little. Peter Ustinov, all bearded that way and brilliant, unable to open his mouth except to say something bright and true, where does he get off trying to make a fool of me that way, by comparison? I don't happen to want to wear a beard, I find a beard like that an unnecessary calling of attention to oneself. And I keep my weight within bounds—*large* bounds, but still bounds. I don't believe it is nice for any man to have more than an average of 20 pounds of blubber to carry around and laugh with whenever he is embarrassed about his bad jokes. I carry a proper average of only 20 pounds of blubber, which in itself is superiority. But not just Ustinov, all of these guys from London, from England, from Wales, from Scotland, from Ireland. What was it with Brendan Behan, singing those irrelevant ballads all the time? Talking all the time, not letting anybody else get in a few quick words, and then when they did, refusing to listen. That isn't the way. That's a very impolite way to be an entity. I always give the other kid a chance to say his say, stupid as I always know it is going to be, and as it always *is.* Kenneth Tynan, or Ken as so many of his admirers prefer to call him, where did he ever come from, with all that fancy writing about the theater? I've got more theater in my little finger than Kenneth Tynan has got in his apposable thumb, which I have just lately learned is the difference between us and the apes. He's got his apposable thumb and I've got mine, but I swear it isn't arrogance that impels me to point out that mine is the superior apposable thumb, it is simple devotion to the truth. These kids won't stop. They keep coming at you from everywhere, from all directions, and some of them seem to drop out of the sky or come up out of holes in the ground, all eager and swift, and none of them aware, as I am, of the difficulty and enormity of the present human predicament. They get the publicity, just the same, even Irving Lazar, and he's not even a writer, he's just an *agent* for writers, he can't even write a letter, he telephones, so he's in *The Saturday Evening Post* with a great big feature story—Irving Lazar. Is Irving Lazar as great a man as Sam Spiegel, who made the movie of Lawrence of Arabia and is a greater man than Lawrence of Arabia, and has a yacht? And pays taxes? And could buy a whole fleet of London taxis if he felt like it? Well, I'm bigger than Sam, everybody knows that, and I'm not referring to height alone, although I'm bigger there, too. I'm referring to size in ineffables, but, if that's not good enough, in *effables*, too. I don't begrudge Irving and Sam having what they have. I'm all for it, if that's the sort of thing they want, all I'm saying is what the hell is the yacht *for*? From the four corners of the world year after year fourflushers keep arriving on the scene and grabbing all the attention and money. It's not right. It's wrong. It hurts. Makes me stop and wonder if all of my noble work has been worth the while. Or did I throw the pearls right smack into the kissers of the pigs? It's not nice even to suspect that I may have.

Put it this way, or as nearly this way as you can possibly manage: A hundred years from now, in 2064, where are all of these kids going to be, and then honestly guess or estimate or compute on a machine where I will be, and then I think you'll understand some of my annoyance, because, frankly, it isn't possible for any outsider to understand *all* of it. Even an insider, and I am very nearly the only insider there is, can't understand all of it. Or *don't* plunge a hundred years forward, make it a smaller portion of time, make it day after tomorrow, because tomorrow is just a little too near—well, where are these kids going to be day after tomorrow? Pretty much nowhere, wouldn't you say? While I am going to be right where I always have been, at the tippy-tip top, alone, aloof, supreme, and still in need of a haircut.

Norman Mailer—why should so many people feel, especially the young, that Norman Mailer is the man who has got something to say to them, and not I? I can't account for it. It simply has got to be the consequence of some sort of unfortunate misunderstanding of something or other. So far he doesn't seem to have encouraged anybody to refer to him by the lovable nickname of Norm, but that in itself doesn't justify the belief so many kids have that Mailer has the message they want to hear. He can write, nobody in his right mind, nobody in anybody's right mind, wants to pretend he can't write, but let's face up to asking the key question at this point: Can he write, can he even begin to write, as I can write, as I have written? Let's just ask that key question, and then let's just try to answer it honestly. He keeps getting all kinds of complicated things straighter than all of the other kids, but the complicated things I write about are even more complicated than the ones he writes about, and I get mine straighter than he gets his. I get mine so straight I have to guard against their moving back over on the other side. And Nelson Algren—what is this wild stuff about Chicago, is Chicago some kind of zoo, or what? And going around the world, and meeting different people—that's a matter of travel, that isn't preaching the gospel. I preach the gospel. And yet these kids are getting all the gravy. And they keep coming—Heller, I can't even remember his first name, *Catch 22*. I never even read it, although there is a kid in there by the name of Yossarian, but the kid's not even an Armenian, let alone me. It just isn't possible for anybody who isn't an Armenian to have the name of Yossarian. One of the hottest writers going, and all on the strength of one novel about how a kid in the Army discovered that an Army is made up of a lot of frightened phonies, each of whom is slyly fighting off accident and death with every ounce of his animal cunning. Something Heller, a name before Heller, but not a nickname, a straight name of some kind. I was in London one time and every newspaper in town had a piece about him, and not a lousy word about me, stopping at the Savoy. J. D. Salinger aching with love for his classy, glassy people, whose family name *is* Glass, but loathing everybody else, as if everybody else were in fact in another race entirely—crooks, charlatans, killers. There's another kid who keeps grabbing—space, fame, money, and all he does is hide, all he does is refuse to see anybody, so everybody keeps trying to get a big story about him just the same. Burns me up. What am I supposed to be, a has-been? A never-was? A second-rater? I don't get it. How can anything so plain as my incomparable superiority go so unnoticed? I have never been cheap. I have always had a cheerful word for just about anybody, children who tend to turn away in terror from most people run to me, even though I look like hell most of the time. And I think about big things earnestly. I worry about the world. I seriously question the wisdom of having a lot of high explosives stockpiled all over the place and ready at a moment's notice. Kids in the Government get a lot of notice, too. They go on television, on *Meet the Press,* on *Open End,* on the Jackie Gleason show, on *Open*

Mind, on *Open Window*, and they casually, playing it down, let everybody know it is only a matter of a small mistake, a nervous accident, until everything will be shot. A lot of high explosives stockpiled all over the place makes me worry as much as it makes anybody else worry. I mean, it isn't all poetry with me, as it is with Ezra Pound, for instance, some of it is anxiety about the whole mother human race. I don't want that race to be blown to smithereens, because a thing like that could make a lot of trouble for me personally and for all I know forever prevent the true greatness of the human race from emerging from the junk pile where it's been for so long. If everything and everybody becomes part of that junk pile, how the hell will I ever make it clear once and for all that I got entangled in the junk by unhappy accident, and by rights should have been out in the light, standing straight on the pedestal plainly marked The Greatest. I worry about that, too. And I hate all these kids who don't worry about big things at all. It isn't right. I'm jealous of all these kids, because if anybody deserves to be lucky, I deserve to be. And I'm suspicious of everybody who seriously imagines that these kids are possibly as important as I am, which on the face of it is fantastic. I am the greatest. Let's just understand that. Let's just accept it, so that we won't become neurotic, and then let's all pitch in together and be nice. Let's all be nice to one another, for as much as ye are nice to one another, ye are nice to me, and ye know me. I'm the nicest. I love everybody.

Malibu 1954

Malibu 1954 is one of a number of poems written while I lived on the beach at Malibu. Another, Long Song, is a large work that I was never able to feel was going well, so it was finally abandoned. I find it difficult to be satisfied with any writing while it is being written, but this feeling is so nearly overwhelming when the writing aspires to poety that I seldom bother to start a poem, although now and then it is unavoidable.

lizards go to morning light
what they think God knows
I can't guess unless it's yes
what matter what lizards think
on their way from shade to shine

what they're not is something else
moles dragonflies worms mice
a withheld meaning almost told
they live or whatever it is
outside my door inside my sleep

I watch lizards watching me
wide-awake and fast-asleep

a fearless frightful calling of a bird
Poe might have liked had he liked day
started at noon with a letter of hate

you write such letters when you must
I guess you do because I do and mail them too
very near politeness done to death

the unseen bird called and wrote
a letter of another order
I thought it must be love

a call to light I thought
in romp in tease in fight in flight
call again and all of it again

a call to play and song
to better things than wrong
but I was wrong again

when the letter was done
and I was done
with courtesy my friend

out the door and down the stairs
somebody went to the sea
and it was very possibly me

someone saw the fearless caller at the end
dead and read his farewell note
so long is all it said my friend

a small white bird
a hundred of his kind fed in the tide
who hadn't died

so long white black or red
hate is just as good as love
as long as you're not dead

the phone buzzes
I'm opposed to bells
I have them buzz instead
bells are for burglaries

hello I say
the lizards wait in the light
the caller lies on a cool clean bed
something I surely must have read

all white all right
fine feet fine beak fine eyes
I'd like somebody to show me
a more fitly-made head

his kind fly in and call
feed find fly out and fall
and call no more as Poe might say
yes sir I say

how about the money you owe
nobody calls to say hello
another of his kind then screams
hello and screams again

in fun of feeding and needing more
I'll pay that money and maybe more
I always do my friend so long
I said so long my friend

back to the beach it's like a bank
it's all money out there
sand seaweed pebbles shells
all coins and currency

glassy globs of living stuff
with thin red lines in glassy fat
bloody eyes near mouth and gut
washed up all washed up

all money where the shore birds feed
where the tide chases time chasing the tide
the birds choose time and time again
where to go to get their own

right there you'll find your fortune
alive and swift but rivet fast
into the watery present past and future
feather fin foot eye and fight itself

it's all money out there
all fame and forty kinds of fortune
a pebble half the size of an egg
worth its weight in human thought

the very invention of matter
green gray black white
where were you last night?
in the sea on the moon in sleep

a rock twice the size of the human head
a perfect word for a white bird's end
the best life never knows what death is
never draws the line always was and never knew

word or bird there's your fortune right there
to know and never know
there's your fame scrambling in the sand
soft-shell scared to death of soft-shell's hell

a little thing more fitly-made
than heaven itself which is much too mean and grand
safe again in the wet and hiding sand
itself still and still afraid

that was day and this is night
or if you like the other way around
the lizard's hidden in the lizard's ground
the fearless caller's on his back
the tide rocks time and rocks together
to work for more of more instead of less of less
if it isn't ever really no
neither is it ever really yes
if you like things either
very clear or not at all
neither

but on my oath
it could be both

All in One Crack

All in One Crack is a play that is not concluded. It could easily be concluded, but there is so much to write and not quite forever in which to do so that I find it pleasant not to see everything through to a smashing net profit of at least a million dollars, as all sensible playwrights like to do. Written in 1955, I believe.

Boob's parlor, to show his brilliance, importance, and wealth, Part-church, part-bank, part-school, part-doctor's office, part-railroad station, part-dock, and so on: crucifix, stained glass window, model trains, model ships, skeleton, full-size picture of the human body, female and male by turns as required.

Boob is old but hard as a rock. His secretary Phil is also old, but the opposite of Boob entirely: thin, feeble, sick.

Boob: (Dictating a letter) Thus, then, we continue with God's guidance. And signed of course, in the usual manner.

Phil: Will you sign, or will I?

Boob: How shall I take that question?

Phil: I mean you have dictated almost a hundred letters.

Boob: Yes, of course, a greeting to all of my people on the occasion of my sixty-ninth birthday. They are heartened by it, but what has the signing got to do with it?

Phil: Simply, will you *be* here?

Boob: Again, how shall I take that question? All you mean, most likely, is do I expect to travel, but I'm not sure. What do you mean?

Phil: Precisely that. Are you reading meanings into everything I say again? Well, there is no need to, I assure you.

Boob: The *tone* is what I am going by, not the words. The words never mean anything, really. Tone is what we understand. Tone is how we make ourselves understood. My tone now with you is patient, courteous, sincere, as befits a man in my position speaking to his faithful secretary. I said faithful in the proper tone. You cannot suspect that I do not mean faithful when I say faithful. But when you say will you *be* here, I feel you are actually hoping that I may not be, that I may be dead. I don't like feeling you may be hoping that I shall soon die.

Phil: Your health is perfect. Always has been. Mine isn't, never has been. If anybody's going, it's more likely to be me, isn't it?

Boob: That isn't the question. Are you hoping I shall die, or not?

Phil: I'd better start typing the letters.

Boob: You'll do no such thing. Answer the question.

Phil: And what about your tone, now?

Boob: I'm angry. I make no bones about it. Yes or no, but be sure it's the truth.

Phil: No.

Boob: I don't believe you.

Phil: I can't help that.

Boob: But you *can*.

Phil: How?

Boob: Tone. Tone. Tone. Now, we know each of us wants to bury everybody else. Perfectly normal, perfectly natural, quite inevitable actually, nothing to be ashamed of. I've buried almost all of my enemies, and I have been glad to bury them, even when I have wept bitterly. One misses one's enemies far more than one does one's friends. But why should you, you of all people, my childhood friend, my faithful secretary precisely half a century, why should you want me to die? There is nothing in my will for you, as you know. You wrote it.

Phil: And rewrote it.

Boob: And rewrote it. I must have a new will every year.

Phil: Every month, but it is actually never new. No, sir, I don't wish you to die.

Boob: You say so, but the tone isn't right, it just isn't right. It does not compel belief. Quite the contrary.

Phil: Perhaps it's yourself. I can only speak truthfully. Perhaps I ought to call the doctor. Perhaps you ought to have another talk with him. Thrash it out again. Others may want you to die, but I don't. Why should I? Is it possible you are the one who wants you to die?

Boob: You speak as if I were two people.

Phil: You speak as if you had no idea you are a good many more than two.

Boob: I have sides, but they are all one—me. And no, I don't want to die. What's more, I don't want you to die, either.

Phil: I really don't have time to think about it, although now and then in my sleep I can feel the awakening of a love for it.

Boob: A love for death?

Phil: For whatever it is. I don't know what death is, what it is to die, I've never died, but lately in my sleep I have noticed a strange smiling in the direction of that ignorance.

Boob: Well, it's a good thing it's almost time for lunch, because I don't want to talk to you when your intelligence is at a low ebb.

Phil: Shall I order it, then?

Boob: I have always had my lunch brought here, why do you suddenly ask if you should order it?

Phil: I have not asked it suddenly. I ask every day. Let me call the doctor.

Boob: Do you really think I need him?

Phil: You're giving meanings to everything I say, of course you need him. Before lunch or after?

Boob: How about neither, how about *that*?

Phil: As you say.

Boob: How do you mean that?

Phil: I refuse to answer. The usual lunch, I presume. Pig with apple in mouth. White wine. Fresh-baked bread. Oranges.

Boob: Oranges is the secret of my stamina. Two large oranges after a meal and you can't go wrong. The citrus of it cuts the fat. What are you going to have?

Phil: A pill and a cup of coffee.

Boob: You get no pleasure from food?

Phil: Unwittingly, perhaps.

Boob: Is that a criticism of the heartiness with which I eat?

Phil: It is not. For God's sake, let me call the doctor.

Boob: Well, call him, then. After lunch. I know when I need help and when I don't, and I don't now, but as long as you keep nagging at me about it, I'll see the doctor, I'll see him, I'll talk to him. Your theory is that now I'm afraid of dying, is that right?

Phil: As you were last time, and the time before and as long as I can remember.

Making Money

Making Money is one of 21 short plays in a group entitled 21 Very Short Plays. It is number 14 as a matter of fact, and one of my favorites. That's why it's here. I find it funny, but I must remark that a number of very good editors don't agree. Well, that's what makes great literature, as we say. Six or seven friends telling one another in print that each of them is the greatest going—and *voila*, eminence, or should one say mincemeat? Let the reader decide—I say this is a very funny play. If you find it funny, too, please tell somebody, because I never knew anybody yet who didn't want to know about a piece of funny writing. What I mean is everybody likes something that makes him laugh. (It was written in 1956, I think.)

Teacher

Now, at this school, which is not unlike a Sunday School, we are to learn how to make money. Why do we wish to make money?

Boy

Because we need money.

Teacher

What do we need money *for*?

Girl

For food and rent and clothes and stuff.

Teacher

What kind of money do we need?

224

Boy

United States.

Teacher

Here, then, for each of you to examine is five dollars of United States money. What is it made out of?

Girl

Some kind of paper.

Teacher

Whose picture is on it?

Boy

Lincoln.

Teacher

What is the picture on the reverse side?

Girl

Lincoln Memorial.

Teacher

In order to make five dollars, what must we do?

Boy

Make another piece of paper look exactly like this piece.

Teacher

How can we do this?

Girl

By some kind of complicated printing and photoengraving.

Teacher

Which is?

Boy

Hard to do.

Teacher

Which also is?

Girl

Against the law.

Teacher

Illegal, we say. Legal with il before it means not legal. In order to have one hundred dollars worth of money how many of these pieces of paper must we make?

Boy

Twenty.

Teacher

A thousand dollars?

Girl

Two hundred.

Teacher

If we wanted a hundred thousand dollars, how many of these pieces of paper would we need to make?

Boy

A hundred times two hundred, whatever that is.

Teacher

A great many pieces of this piece of paper. In order to have five million dollars we would need to make one million of these pieces of paper. How little is five million dollars?

Girl

Five million dollars isn't a little, but it is less than the number of dollars many American families have.

Teacher

Can you name some of these families?

Boy

Ford, Rockefeller, Kennedy.

Teacher

How did these families *get* five million dollars? Twenty-five million? A hundred and twenty-five million?

Girl

They made the money.

Teacher

And what are we here to learn to do?

Boy

To make money.

Teacher

How much money?

Boy

Five million dollars. A million for me, a million for her, a million for you, a million for him, a million for her.

Teacher

A million apiece.

Girl

Tax free.

Boy
Illegal.

Girl
But neat.

Teacher
Our figures are based upon units of five. These are other units. Name several.

Boy
Ten. Twenty. Fifty. One hundred.

Teacher
Ten, twenty, fifty, one hundred? One moment, please. I believe I have an idea. Can anyone guess what the idea is?

Girl
Let's not make fives, let's make hundreds.

Teacher
Precisely. Using less paper we shall have more money. Some for my father, some for my mother. If we make a million of these hundreds we will have a hundred million, or twenty times as much as five million. Will that make us happy?

Boy
Yes.

Teacher
I am delighted about having gotten the idea because it means so much more money for so many more of us. So let me hear it.

Everybody
Yaaaaay.

Teacher
Again. Louder.

Everybody
Yaaaaaaaaay.

Teacher
It's terribly thrilling, I must say. In addition to my father and my mother, I am sure I shall want to give a million each to my son, my daughter, my son-in-law, my daughter-in-law, and something for the poor.

Boy
I've got some people I want to give a million to, also, and something for Alexander.

Girl

A million each to my father, my mother, my grandfather, my grand-mother, Margaret, and something for World Peace.

Teacher

This is indeed a great thrill.

Everybody

Yaaaaaay.

Boy

Teacher?

Teacher

Yes, my boy?

Boy

Isn't there a piece of paper for one *thousand* dollars?

Everybody

Yaaaaaaay.

Teacher

Just a minute, everybody. If there *is* such a piece of paper, and if we make a million of that—

Girl

There *is* such a piece. I saw it on television.

Teacher

A thousand million dollars, children?

Everybody

Yaaaaaaay.

Teacher

It fairly staggers the imagination.

Everybody

Yaaaaay.

Teacher

There will be a million apiece to give to—I'll give a million to Miss Leatherbridge.

Everybody

Yaaaaay.

Teacher

That is our first lesson, then, children. I want to sit down now and brood about this.

Everybody

Yaaaaaay.

Teacher

The management of great wealth is a great responsibility.

Everybody

Yaaaay.

Teacher

Schools, hospitals, mental institutions.

Everybody

Yaaaay.

Teacher

Go home now, then, and let me sit here and brood.

Everybody

Yaaaaaay.

(They go)

Teacher

I'd like a small island. Not Cuba necessarily. But a nice island with a nice population. The children—well, to them it's a game. Still, the boy *did* think of the one-thousand principle. An ice cream soda for the others, and two for him. That will be ample. Too much money for the poor spoils them. A thousand million for me I think will just about do it.

(Softly)

Yaaaaaay.

I Used to Believe
I Had Forever
Now I'm Not So Sure

I Used to Believe I Had Forever Now I'm Not So Sure is another play that is deliberately not concluded: such a play occurs to me every day, but only now and then do I bother to get the first part of it on paper. This time I did, and I'm glad I did, because this play pleases me. 1961?

Death Row, San Quentin: a gangling Preacher is let into a cell.

Preacher: All right now, my boy—nothing to be afraid of.

Pete: Never mind *that*, Pop. Are you a Holy Roller? First things first. Holy Roller, or I die plain.

Preacher: I belong to the Church of Light.

Pete: I want a Holy Roller. I made that perfectly clear. First they sent me a Catholic, and I can't stand 'em. He wants to argue. If it's good enough for the President—well, it's *not* good enough for me. I felt sorry for him. He was so eager to make good, but I refused him, and we know what that means, Pop, don't we? That's refusing Baby Jesus, too, isn't it? Well, I did it. I refused them *both*. Holy Roller or not, Pop? Yes or no?

Preacher: Church of Light, my boy. Church of Light.

Pete: *Out,* then. No Church of Light in here. I can die like an amateur. So long, Pop. Take care of yourself.

Preacher: (A kind of sudden moan-song) Oh, Lord of Light, behold this man.

Pete: Now you're talking, Pop.

Preacher: (Higher, more lunatic) Lord, Lord, Lord of Light, look here. Look look, look here, look here.

Pete: Tell him, Pop.

Preacher: We've got here in this cell in Death Row in San Quentin in the state of California a man, oh Lord.

Pete: Make it good, Pop, and you've got yourself a deal.

Preacher: A man of sin, oh Lord. He sinned, he sinned bad. (Aside almost, normal voice) Murder, was it, son?

Pete: Rape and kidnap, but never mind the crime.

Preacher: He kidnapped, oh Lord, and then he raped.

Pete: Right, Pop. So then after the Catholic, they sent an Episcopalian wanting me to be sorry and a child and a great man and the Ambassador to the Moon or something, so I threw him out, too. You're no preacher, Pop, you're a con man. That Church of Light's part of your con, isn't it?

Preacher: (Song-style of speech) He wants to know, oh Lord, am I a real preacher, and I say yes, yes Lord, yess, oh yesss Lord, yess.

Pete: How long you been in the racket?

Preacher: (Song-style) Going on three years now, Lord, I been in the racket, praying and converting.

Pete: (Song-style) And flipping the quif.

Preacher: Yes, Lord, flipping the quif.

Pete: (Song-style) In thy holy name. (Normal voice) However.

Preacher: Yes, Lord, in thy holy name. Everything I do, Lord, is in thy holy name.

Pete: Man, I don't mind *this* at all. If you've got to be saved, this is the way all right. Come on, Pop, I won't interrupt any more. Go right ahead and do your stuff and then let's have the transfer. I'll go smiling.

Preacher: First, he kidnapped, oh Lord, and then he raped, and now they're going to sit him down in the little room and turn on the gas. He's a good boy, Lord, just a little strong. If I had seen him in time he could have joined the church and made good.

Pete: I would *have* joined, too. Religious quif is the best quif.

Preacher: He knows the truth, oh Lord.

Warden (arrives): The Governor's given you a postponement, Pete.

Pete: Are you kidding, Warden?

Warden: No, I just talked to him on the phone. That's all, Reverend.

Preacher: (Song-style) I thank you, oh Lord.

Pete: I'd like him to stay a minute, Warden.

Warden: Five minutes, then, Pete, but that's all.

Pete: O.K. (Warden goes.) All right, now, Pop, relax. Let's talk. You kind of remind me of somebody I should have met long ago—say, like my father. What's your name?

Preacher: Wendell Cook.

Pete: Where you from?

Preacher: Pismo Beach.

Pete: When did you start this preaching racket?

Preacher: I been preaching at the church three years now.

Pete: Plenty of easy women day after day and night after night?

Preacher: Enough for all of us, praise the Lord.

Pete: I had an idea there was something wrong with my approach. Well, it's too late now. Pop, do me a favor.

Preacher: What is it, my boy?

Pete: Come back tomorrow with a girl, not more than thirteen, dressed like a boy. Oh, don't worry, I just want to *smell* her. Tell 'em she's your son, or my kid brother or something. Choose the right girl, you know what I mean, Pop. One you *know* is right. Will you do that?

Preacher: I know just the girl. It won't be easy to make her look like a boy. (Looks around.) Is there anywhere in this cell I might turn my back for five or six minutes?

Pete: Hell, Pop, I could do it standing up if it came to *that*, but that's not what I'm thinking about at all.

Preacher: Yes, I know, but the minute she's here that's the *only* thing you *will* be thinking about, and I'd like it to be kind of right for you, and for her, too.

Pete: By God, you're not kidding, are you, Pop?

Preacher: No, I'm against capital punishment. Used to be they only killed murderers, but now it's kidnap and rape, too.

Pete: The worst of it is I didn't *know* it was kidnap. And if it *was* rape, it was the same as when it hadn't been rape. I mean, I was informed afterwards.

Preacher: I don't believe you should be killed for *that*.

Pete: In some countries I'd be decorated, but then I'm an American. Tell me about her.

Preacher: We call her Dolly. She's got a little color—about a fifth, I guess. You don't object to that?

Pete: Hell no, *prefer* it. But you can't mean a *fifth,* you mean a fourth or an eighth, don't you?

Preacher: (Brings bottle from back pocket) I wasn't thinking. (Hands bottle to Pete, who takes swig.)

Pete: Pop, you're a killer. If I could have chosen my father, you'd be him.

Preacher: I've got boys, I've got a *lot* of boys.

Pete: I'll bet you have.

Preacher: And girls, too.

Pete: I'll bet you have, Pop.

Preacher: One apiece from various women in many families, all happily adjusted.

Pete: Ah, they'll all be grand men and women, no doubt about that.

Preacher: You get Dolly with child and I'll see your child gets properly brought up.

Pete: Pop, I'm *not* going to jump Dolly.

Preacher: You never know. You've been away from the dear things a year now, haven't you? Well, let's wait until Dolly's here.

Pete: O.K., Pop.

Preacher: And I'm going to pray for you.

Pete: Cut it, Pop, we're friends.

Preacher: Oh, I know it's silly, especially from a man like me, but it can't do any harm, my boy. And I get *ideas* when I pray.

Pete: I'll bet you do. Who to jump next?

Preacher: Yes, but other ideas, too. There's a way to keep you from being killed. I may find out *how* while I'm praying.

Pete: Not California, Pop. They've tried every which way here and it doesn't work. Take what's his name, just a couple of years ago, had the whole world hollering to spare his life, didn't do him any good.

Preacher: Yes, I believe I heard about the poor man.

Pete: Don't waste your sympathy.

Preacher: But you didn't know him, did you?

Pete: I know a hundred who did.

Preacher: They didn't like him?

Pete: If the State had spared him, they *wouldn't* have.

Preacher: There must have been some sort of a reason, I suppose. (Voice: All right, Reverend, time now.) Well, my boy, untill tomorrow at four, with Dolly dressed like a boy. I don't know how we're going to do that, really.

Pete: Before you go, Pop. Give me a little of the Holy Roller stuff, will you?

Preacher: (Song-speech) Oh, Lord of Light, we thank you for the postponement. Let the Governor win the nomination for President, and let the women grow in grace. (The preacher goes.)

Pete: Amen, Pop.